MATH 500
Teacher's Guide

Author:

Glynlyon Staff

Editor:

Alan Christopherson, M.S.

804 N. 2nd Ave. E.
Rock Rapids, IA 51246-1759

MATH 500

LIFEPAC® Overview

MATH SCOPE & SEQUENCE

KINDERGARTEN

Lessons 1-40	Lessons 41-80	Lessons 81-120	Lessons 121-160
Directions - right, left, high, low, etc.	**Directions** - right, left, high, low, etc.	**Directions** - right, left, high, low, etc.	**Directions** - right, left, high, low, etc.
Comparisons - big, little, alike, different	**Comparisons** - big, little, alike, different	**Comparisons** - big, little, alike, different	**Comparisons** - big, little, alike, different
Matching	**Matching**	**Matching**	**Matching**
Cardinal Numbers - to 9	**Cardinal Numbers** - to 12	**Cardinal Numbers** - to 19	**Cardinal Numbers** - to 100
Colors - red, blue, green, yellow, brown, purple	**Colors** - orange	**Colors** - black, white	**Colors** - pink
Shapes - circle, square, rectangle, triangle	**Shapes** - circle, square, rectangle, triangle	**Shapes** - circle, square, rectangle, triangle	**Shapes** - circle, square, rectangle, triangle
Number Order	**Number Order**	**Number Order**	**Number Order**
Before and After	**Before and After**	**Before and After**	**Before and After**
Ordinal Numbers - to 9th	**Ordinal Numbers** - to 9th	**Ordinal Numbers** - to 9th	**Ordinal Numbers** - to 9th
Problem Solving	**Problem Solving**	**Problem Solving**	**Problem Solving**
	Number Words - to nine	**Number Words** - to nine	**Number Words** - to nine
	Addition - to 9	**Addition** - multiples of 10	**Addition** - to 10 and multiples of 10
		Subtraction - to 9	**Subtraction** - to 10
		Place Value	**Place Value**
		Time/Calendar	**Time/Calendar**
			Money
			Skip Counting - 2's, 5's, 10's
			Greater/Less Than

MATH SCOPE & SEQUENCE

	Grade 1	Grade 2	Grade 3
UNIT 1	**NUMBER ORDER, ADD/SUBTRACT** • Number order, skip-count • Add, subtract to 9 • Story problems • Measurements • Shapes	**NUMBERS AND WORDS TO 100** • Numbers and words to 100 • Operation symbols: +, –, =, >, < • Add and subtract • Place value and fact families • Story problems	**ADD/SUB TO 18 AND PLACE VALUE** • Digits, place value to 999 • Add and subtract • Linear measurements • Operation symbols: +, –, =, ≠, >, < • Time
UNIT 2	**ADD/SUBTRACT TO 10, SHAPES** • Add, subtract to 10 • Number words • Place value • Patterns, sequencing, estimation • Shapes	**ADD/SUBTRACT AND EVEN/ODD** • Numbers and words to 200 • Add, subtract, even and odd • Skip-count 2s, 5s, and 10s • Ordinal numbers, fractions, and money • Shapes	**CARRYING AND BORROWING** • Fact families, patterns, and fractions • Add and subtract with carrying and borrowing • Skip count 2s, 5s, 10s • Money, shapes, lines • Even and odd
UNIT 3	**FRACTIONS, TIME, AND SYMBOLS** • Number sentences • Fractions • Story problems • Time and the = symbol • Oral directions	**ADD WITH CARRYING TO THE 10'S PLACE** • Add with carrying to the 10's place • Subtract • Flat shapes, money, A.M./P.M. • Rounding to the 10's place • Standard measurements	**FACTS OF ADD/SUB AND FRACTIONS** • Add 3 numbers w/ carrying • Coins, weight, volume, A.M./P.M. • Fractions • Skip count 3s, subtract w/ borrowing • Oral instructions
UNIT 4	**ADD TO 18, MONEY, MEASUREMENT** • Add to 18 • Skip-count, even and odd • Money • Shapes and measurement • Place value	**NUMBERS/WORDS TO 999, AND GRAPHS** • Numbers and words to 999 • Addition, subtraction, and place value • Calendar • Measurements and solid shapes • Making change	**ROUND, ESTIMATE, STORY PROBLEMS** • Place value to 9,999 • Rounding to the 10's and estimating • Add and subtract fractions • Roman numerals • 1/4 inch
UNIT 5	**COLUMN ADDITION AND ESTIMATION** • Add three 1-digit numbers • Ordinal numbers • Time and number lines • Estimation and charts • Fractions	**ADD/SUBTRACT TO THE 100'S PLACE** • Data and bar graphs and shapes • Add and subtract to the 100's • Skip-count 3s and place value to the 100's • Add fractions • Temperature	**PLANE SHAPES AND SYMMETRY** • Number sentences • Rounding to the 100's and estimation • Perimeter and square inch • Bar graph, symmetry, and even/odd rules • Temperature
UNIT 6	**NUMBER WORDS TO 99** • Number words to 99 • Add two 2-digit numbers • Symbols: > and < • Fractions • Shapes	**SUBTRACT WITH BORROWING FROM 10'S** • Measurements • Time and money • Subtract w/ borrowing from the 10's place • Add and subtract fractions • Perimeter	**MULTIPLICATION, LINES, AND ANGLES** • Add and subtract to 9,999 • Multiples and multiplication facts for 2 • Area and equivalent fractions • Line graphs, segments, and angles • Money
UNIT 7	**COUNT TO 200, SUBTRACT TO 12** • Number order and place value • Subtract to 12 • Operation signs • Estimation and time • Graphs	**ADD WITH CARRYING TO THE 100'S PLACE** • Add with carrying to the 100's place • Fractions as words • Number order in books • Rounding and estimation	**ADD/SUB MIXED NUMBERS, PROBABILITY** • Multiplication facts for 5 and missing numbers • Add and subtract mixed numbers • Subtract with 0s in the minuend • Circle graphs • Probability
UNIT 8	**ADD/SUBTRACT TO 18** • Addition, subtract to 18 • Group counting • Fractions • Time and measurements • Shapes	**VOLUME AND COIN CONVERSION** • Addition, subtraction, and measurements • Group counting and "thinking" answers • Convert coins • Directions – North, South, East, and West. • Length and width	**MEASUREMENTS AND MULTIPLICATION** • Multiplication facts for 3 & 10, multiples of 4 • Convert units of measurement • Decimals and directions • Picture graphs and missing addends • Length and width
UNIT 9	**SENSIBLE ANSWERS** • Fact families • Sensible answers • Subtract 2-digit numbers • Add three 2-digit numbers	**AREA/SQUARE MEASUREMENT** • Area and square measurement • Add three 2-digit numbers with carrying • Add coins and convert to cents • Fractions and quarter-inches	**MULT, METRICS, AND PERIMETER** • Add and subtract whole numbers, fractions, and mixed numbers • Standard measurements and metrics • Operation symbols • Multiplication facts for 4
UNIT 10	**REVIEW** • Addition, subtraction, and place value • Directions – North, South, East, and West. • Fractions • Patterns	**REVIEW** • Rules for even and odd numbers • Round numbers to the 100's place • Digital clocks and sensible answers • Add three 3-digit numbers	**PROBABILITY, UNITS, AND SHAPES** • Addition and subtraction • Rounding to the 1,000's place and estimating • Probability, equations, and parentheses • Perimeter and area • Multiplication facts for 2, 3, 4, 5, and 10

MATH SCOPE & SEQUENCE

Grade 4	Grade 5	Grade 6	
WHOLE NUMBERS AND FRACTIONS • Naming whole numbers • Naming fractions • Sequencing patterns • Numbers to 1,000	**PLACE VALUE, ADDITION, AND SUBTRACTION** • Place value • Rounding and estimating • Addition • Subtraction	**WHOLE NUMBERS AND ALGEBRA** • Whole numbers and their properties • Operations and number patterns • Algebra	UNIT 1
MULTIPLYING WHOLE NUMBERS • Operation symbols • Multiplication — 1-digit multipliers • Addition and subtraction of fractions • Numbers to 10,000	**MULTIPLYING WHOLE NUMBERS AND DECIMALS** • Multiplying whole numbers • Powers • Multiplying decimals	**DATA ANALYSIS** • Collecting and describing data • Organizing data • Displaying and interpreting data	UNIT 2
SEQUENCING AND ROUNDING • Multiplication with carrying • Rounding and estimation • Sequencing fractions • Numbers to 100,000	**DIVIDING WHOLE NUMBERS AND DECIMALS** • One-digit divisors • Two-digit divisors • Decimal division	**DECIMALS** • Decimal numbers • Multiplying and dividing decimal numbers • The metric system	UNIT 3
LINES AND SHAPES • Plane and solid shapes • Lines and line segments • Addition and subtraction • Multiplication with carrying	**ALGEBRA AND GRAPHING** • Expressions • Functions • Equations • Graphing	**FRACTIONS** • Factors and fractions • The LCM and fractions • Decimals and fractions	UNIT 4
DIVISION AND MEASUREMENTS • Division – 1-digit divisor • Families of facts • Standard measurements • Number grouping	**MEASUREMENT** • The metric system • The customary system • Time • Temperature	**FRACTION OPERATIONS** • Adding and subtracting fractions • Multiplying and dividing fractions • The customary system	UNIT 5
DIVISION, FACTORS, AND FRACTIONS • Division — 1-digit divisors with remainders • Factors and multiples • Improper and mixed fractions • Equivalent fractions	**FACTORS AND FRACTIONS** • Factors • Equivalent fractions • Fractions	**RATIO, PROPORTION, AND PERCENT** • Ratios • Proportions • Percent	UNIT 6
WHOLE NUMBERS AND FRACTIONS • Multiplication — 2-digit multipliers • Simplifying fractions • Averages • Decimals in money problems • Equations	**FRACTION OPERATIONS** • Like denominators • Unlike denominators • Multiplying fractions • Dividing fractions	**PROBABILITY AND GEOMETRY** • Probability • Geometry: Angles • Geometry: Polygons	UNIT 7
WHOLE NUMBERS AND FRACTIONS • Division — 1-digit divisors • Fractions and unlike denominators • Metric units • Whole numbers: +, –, x, ÷	**DATA ANALYSIS AND PROBABILITY** • Collecting data • Analyzing data • Displaying data • Probability	**GEOMETRY AND MEASUREMENT** • Plane figures • Solid figures	UNIT 8
DECIMALS AND FRACTIONS • Reading and writing decimals • Adding and subtracting mixed numbers • Cross multiplication • Estimation	**GEOMETRY** • Geometry • Classifying plane figures • Classifying solid figures • Transformations • Symmetry	**INTEGERS AND TRANSFORMATIONS** • Integers • Integer operations • Transformations	UNIT 9
ESTIMATION, CHARTS, AND GRAPHS • Estimation and data gathering • Charts and graphs • Review numbers to 100,000 • Whole numbers: +, –, x, ÷	**PERIMETER, AREA, AND VOLUME** • Perimeter • Area • Surface area • Volume	**EQUATIONS AND FUNCTIONS** • Equations • More equations and inequalities • Functions	UNIT 10

MATH SCOPE & SEQUENCE

	Grade 7	Grade 8	Grade 9
UNIT 1	**INTEGERS** • Adding and Subtracting Integers • Multiplying and Dividing Integers • The Real Number System	**THE REAL NUMBER SYSTEM** • Relationships • Other Forms • Simplifying	**VARIABLES AND NUMBERS** • Variables • Distributive Property • Definition of signed numbers • Signed number operations
UNIT 2	**FRACTIONS** • Working with Fractions • Adding and Subtracting Fractions • Multiplying and Dividing Fractions	**MODELING PROBLEMS IN INTEGERS** • Equations with Real Numbers • Functions • Integers • Modeling with Integers	**SOLVING EQUATIONS** • Sentences and formulas • Properties • Solving equations • Solving inequalities
UNIT 3	**DECIMALS** • Decimals and Their Operations • Applying Decimals • Scientific Notation • The Metric System	**MODELING PROBLEMS WITH RATIONAL NUMBERS** • Number Theory • Solving Problems with Rational Numbers • Solving Equations and Inequalities	**PROBLEM ANALYSIS AND SOLUTION** • Words and symbols • Simple verbal problems • Medium verbal problems • Challenging verbal problems
UNIT 4	**PATTERNS AND EQUATIONS** • Variable Expressions • Patterns and Functions • Solving Equations • Equations and Inequalities	**PROPORTIONAL REASONING** • Proportions • Percents • Measurement/Similar Figures	**POLYNOMIALS** • Addition of polynomials • Subtraction of polynomials • Multiplication of polynomials • Division of polynomials
UNIT 5	**RATIOS AND PROPORTIONS** • Ratios, Rates, and Proportions • Using Proportions • Fractions, Decimals, and Percents	**MORE WITH FUNCTIONS** • Solving Equations • Families of Functions • Patterns	**ALGEBRAIC FACTORS** • Greatest common factor • Binomial factors • Complete factorization • Word problems
UNIT 6	**PROBABILITY AND GRAPHING** • Probability • Functions • Graphing Linear Equations • Direct Variation	**MEASUREMENT** • Angle Measures and Circles • Polygons • Indirect Measure	**ALGEBRAIC FRACTIONS** • Operations with fractions • Solving equations • Solving inequalities • Solving word problems
UNIT 7	**DATA ANALYSIS** • Describing Data • Organizing Data • Graphing Data and Making Predictions	**PLANE GEOMETRY** • Perimeter and Area • Symmetry and Reflections • Other Transformations	**RADICAL EXPRESSIONS** • Rational and irrational numbers • Operations with radicals • Irrational roots • Radical equations
UNIT 8	**GEOMETRY** • Basic Geometry • Classifying Polygons • Transformations	**MEASURE OF SOLID FIGURES** • Surface Area • Solid Figures • Volume • Volume of Composite Figures	**GRAPHING** • Equations of two variables • Graphing lines • Graphing inequalities • Equations of lines
UNIT 9	**MEASUREMENT AND AREA** • Perimeter • Area • The Pythagorean Theorem	**DATA ANALYSIS** • Collecting and Representing Data • Central Tendency and Dispersion • Frequency and Histograms • Box-and-Whisker Plots • Scatter Plots	**SYSTEMS** • Graphical solution • Algebraic solutions • Determinants • Word problems
UNIT 10	**SURFACE AREA AND VOLUME** • Solids • Prisms • Cylinders	**PROBABILITY** • Outcomes • Permutations and Combinations • Probability and Odds • Independent and Dependent Events	**QUADRATIC EQUATIONS AND REVIEW** • Solving quadratic equations • Equations and inequalities • Polynomials and factors • Radicals and graphing

MATH SCOPE & SEQUENCE

Grade 10	Grade 11	Grade 12	
A MATHEMATICAL SYSTEM • Points, lines, and planes • Definition of definitions • Geometric terms • Postulates and theorems	**SETS, STRUCTURE, AND FUNCTION** • Properties and operations of sets • Axioms and applications • Relations and functions • Algebraic expressions	**RELATIONS AND FUNCTIONS** • Relations and functions • Rules of correspondence • Notation of functions • Types of functions	UNIT 1
PROOFS • Logic • Reasoning • Two-column proof • Paragraph proof	**NUMBERS, SENTENCES, & PROBLEMS** • Order and absolute value • Sums and products • Algebraic sentences • Number and motion problems	**SPECIAL FUNCTIONS** • Linear functions • Second-degree functions • Polynomial functions • Other functions	UNIT 2
ANGLES AND PARALLELS • Definitions and measurement • Relationships and theorems • Properties of parallels • Parallels and polygons	**LINEAR EQUATIONS & INEQUALITIES** • Graphs • Equations • Systems of equations • Inequalities	**TRIGONOMETRIC FUNCTIONS** • Definition • Equation of functions • Trigonometric tables • Special angles	UNIT 3
CONGRUENCY • Congruent triangles • Corresponding parts • Inequalities • Quadrilaterals	**POLYNOMIALS** • Multiplying polynomials • Factoring • Operations with polynomials • Variations	**CIRCULAR FUNCTIONS & GRAPHS** • Circular functions & special angles • Graphs of sin and cosine • Amplitude and period • Phase shifts	UNIT 4
SIMILAR POLYGONS • Ratios and proportions • Definition of similarity • Similar polygons and triangles • Right triangle geometry	**RADICAL EXPRESSIONS** • Multiplying and dividing fractions • Adding and subtracting fractions • Equations with fractions • Applications of fractions	**IDENTITIES AND FUNCTIONS** • Reciprocal relations • Pythagorean relations • Trigonometric identities • Sum and difference formulas	UNIT 5
CIRCLES • Circles and spheres • Tangents, arcs, and chords • Special angles in circles • Special segments in circles	**REAL NUMBERS** • Rational and irrational numbers • Laws of Radicals • Quadratic equations • Quadratic formula	**TRIGONOMETRIC FUNCTIONS** • Trigonometric functions • Law of cosines • Law of sines • Applied problems	UNIT 6
CONSTRUCTION AND LOCUS • Basic constructions • Triangles and circles • Polygons • Locus meaning and use	**QUADRATIC RELATIONS & SYSTEMS** • Distance formulas • Conic sections • Systems of equations • Application of conic sections	**INVERSE TRIGONOMETRIC FUNCTIONS** • Inverse functions • Graphing polar coordinates • Converting polar coordinates • Graphing polar equations	UNIT 7
AREA AND VOLUME • Area of polygons • Area of circles • Surface area of solids • Volume of solids	**EXPONENTIAL FUNCTIONS** • Exponents • Exponential equations • Logarithmic functions • Matrices	**QUADRATIC EQUATIONS** • Conic sections • Circle and ellipse • Parabola and hyperbola • Transformations	UNIT 8
COORDINATE GEOMETRY • Ordered pairs • Distance • Lines • Coordinate proofs	**COUNTING PRINCIPLES** • Progressions • Permutations • Combinations • Probability	**PROBABILITY** • Random experiments & probability • Permutations • Combinations • Applied problems	UNIT 9
REVIEW • Proof and angles • Polygons and circles • Construction and measurement • Coordinate geometry	**REVIEW** • Integers and open sentences • Graphs and polynomials • Fractions and quadratics • Exponential functions	**CALCULUS** • Mathematical induction • Functions and limits • Slopes of functions • Review	UNIT 10

STRUCTURE OF THE LIFEPAC CURRICULUM

The LIFEPAC curriculum is conveniently structured to provide one Teacher's Guide containing teacher support material with answer keys and ten student worktexts for each subject at grade levels 2 through 12. The worktext format of the LIFEPACs allows the student to read the textual information and complete workbook activities all in the same booklet. The easy-to-follow LIFEPAC numbering system lists the grade as the first number(s) and the last two digits as the number of the series. For example, the Language Arts LIFEPAC at the 6th grade level, 5th book in the series would be LAN0605.

Each LIFEPAC is divided into three to five sections and begins with an introduction or overview of the booklet as well as a series of specific learning objectives to give a purpose to the study of the LIFEPAC. The introduction and objectives are followed by a vocabulary section which may be found at the beginning of each section at the lower levels or in the glossary at the high school level. Vocabulary words are used to develop word recognition and should not be confused with the spelling words introduced later in the LIFEPAC. The student should learn all vocabulary words before working the LIFEPAC sections to improve comprehension, retention, and reading skills.

Each activity or written assignment in grades 2 through 12 has a number for easy identification, such as 1.1. The first number corresponds to the LIFEPAC section and the number to the right of the decimal is the number of the activity.

Teacher checkpoints, which are essential to maintain quality learning, are found at various locations throughout the LIFEPAC. The teacher should check 1) neatness of work and penmanship, 2) quality of understanding (tested with a short oral quiz), 3) thoroughness of answers (complete sentences and paragraphs, correct spelling, etc.), 4) completion of activities (no blank spaces), and 5) accuracy of answers as compared to the answer key (all answers correct).

The self test questions in grades 2 through 12 are also number coded for easy reference. For example, 2.015 means that this is the 15th question in the self test of Section 2. The first number corresponds to the LIFEPAC section, the zero indicates that it is a self test question, and the number to the right of the zero the question number.

The LIFEPAC test is packaged at the center of each LIFEPAC. It should be removed and put aside before giving the booklet to the student for study.

Answer and test keys in grades 2 through 12 have the same numbering system as the LIFEPACs. The student may be given access to the answer keys (not the test keys) under teacher supervision so that he can score his own work.

A thorough study of the Scope & Sequence by the teacher before instruction begins is essential to the success of the student. The teacher should become familiar with expected skill mastery and understand how these grade-level skills fit into the overall skill development of the curriculum. The teacher should also preview the objectives that appear at the beginning of each LIFEPAC for additional preparation and planning.

TEST SCORING AND GRADING

Answer keys and test keys give examples of correct answers. They convey the idea, but the student may use many ways to express a correct answer. The teacher should check for the essence of the answer, not for the exact wording. Many questions are high level and require thinking and creativity on the part of the student. Each answer should be scored based on whether or not the main idea written by the student matches the model example. "Any Order" or "Either Order" in a key indicates that no particular order is necessary to be correct.

Most self tests and LIFEPAC tests at the lower elementary levels are scored at 1 point per answer; however, the upper levels may have a point system awarding 2 to 5 points for various answers or questions. Further, the total test points will vary; they may not always equal 100 points. They may be 78, 85, 100, 105, etc.

Example 1

58 / 72   SCORE _____   TEACHER _____ _____
                                                 initials   date

Example 2

84 / 105   SCORE _____   TEACHER _____ _____
                                                  initials   date

A score box similar to ex. 1 above is located at the end of each self test and on the front of the LIFEPAC test. The bottom score, 72, represents the total number of points possible on the test. The upper score, 58, represents the number of points your student will need to receive an 80% or passing grade. If you wish to establish the exact percentage that your student has achieved, find the total points of his correct answers and divide it by the bottom number (in this case 72). For example, if your student has a point total of 65, divide 65 by 72 for a grade of 90%. Referring to ex. 2, on a test with a total of 105 possible points, the student would have to receive a minimum of 84 correct points for an 80% or passing grade. If your student has received 93 points, simply divide the 93 by 105 for a percentage grade of 89%. Students who receive a score below 80% should review the LIFEPAC and retest using the appropriate Alternate Test found in the Teacher's Guide.

The following is a guideline to assign letter grades for completed LIFEPACs based on a maximum total score of 100 points.

Example:

LIFEPAC Test	=	60% of the Total Score (or percent grade)
Self Test	=	25% of the Total Score (average percent of self tests)
Reports	=	10% or 10* points per LIFEPAC
Oral Work	=	5% or 5* points per LIFEPAC

*Determined by the teacher's subjective evaluation of the student's daily work.

Example:

LIFEPAC Test Score	=	92%	92 × .60 = 55 points
Self Test Average	=	90%	90 × .25 = 23 points
Reports			= 8 points
Oral Work			= 4 points

TOTAL POINTS	= 90 points

Grade Scale based on point system:

100 – 94	=	A
93 – 86	=	B
85 – 77	=	C
76 – 70	=	D
Below 70	=	F

TEACHER HINTS AND STUDYING TECHNIQUES

LIFEPAC activities are written to check the level of understanding of the preceding text. The student may look back to the text as necessary to complete these activities; however, a student should never attempt to do the activities without reading (studying) the text first. Self tests and LIFEPAC tests are never open book tests.

Language arts activities (skill integration) often appear within other subject curriculum. The purpose is to give the student an opportunity to test his skill mastery outside of the context in which it was presented.

Writing complete answers (paragraphs) to some questions is an integral part of the LIFEPAC curriculum in all subjects. This builds communication and organization skills, increases understanding and retention of ideas, and helps enforce good penmanship. Complete sentences should be encouraged for this type of activity. Obviously, single words or phrases do not meet the intent of the activity, since multiple lines are given for the response.

Review is essential to student success. Time invested in review where review is suggested will be time saved in correcting errors later. Self tests, unlike the section activities, are closed book. This procedure helps to identify weaknesses before they become too great to overcome. Certain objectives from self tests are cumulative and test previous sections; therefore, good preparation for a self test must include all material studied up to that testing point.

The following procedure checklist has been found to be successful in developing good study habits in the LIFEPAC curriculum.

1. Read the introduction and Table of Contents.
2. Read the objectives.
3. Recite and study the entire vocabulary (glossary) list.
4. Study each section as follows:
   a. Read the introduction and study the section objectives.
   b. Read all the text for the entire section, but answer none of the activities.
   c. Return to the beginning of the section and memorize each vocabulary word and definition.
   d. Reread the section, complete the activities, check the answers with the answer key, correct all errors, and have the teacher check.
   e. Read the self test but do not answer the questions.
   f. Go to the beginning of the first section and reread the text and answers to the activities up to the self test you have not yet done.
   g. Answer the questions to the self test without looking back.
   h. Have the self test checked by the teacher.
   i. Correct the self test and have the teacher check the corrections.
   j. Repeat steps a–i for each section.
5. Use the SQ3R method to prepare for the LIFEPAC test.

   Scan the whole LIFEPAC.
   Question yourself on the objectives.
   Read the whole LIFEPAC again.
   Recite through an oral examination.
   Review weak areas.

6. Take the LIFEPAC test as a closed book test.
7. LIFEPAC tests are administered and scored under direct teacher supervision. Students who receive scores below 80% should review the LIFEPAC using the SQ3R study method and take the Alternate Test located in the Teacher's Guide. The final test grade may be the grade on the Alternate Test or an average of the grades from the original LIFEPAC test and the Alternate Test.

GOAL SETTING AND SCHEDULES

Each school must develop its own schedule, because no single set of procedures will fit every situation. The following is an example of a daily schedule that includes the five LIFEPAC subjects as well as time slotted for special activities.

Possible Daily Schedule

8:15	–	8:25	Pledges, prayer, songs, devotions, etc.
8:25	–	9:10	Bible
9:10	–	9:55	Language Arts
9:55	–	10:15	Recess (juice break)
10:15	–	11:00	Math
11:00	–	11:45	History & Geography
11:45	–	12:30	Lunch, recess, quiet time
12:30	–	1:15	Science
1:15	–		Drill, remedial work, enrichment*

*Enrichment: Computer time, physical education, field trips, fun reading, games and puzzles, family business, hobbies, resource persons, guests, crafts, creative work, electives, music appreciation, projects.

Basically, two factors need to be considered when assigning work to a student in the LIFEPAC curriculum.

The first is time. An average of 45 minutes should be devoted to each subject, each day. Remember, this is only an average. Because of extenuating circumstances a student may spend only 15 minutes on a subject one day and the next day spend 90 minutes on the same subject.

The second factor is the number of pages to be worked in each subject. A single LIFEPAC is designed to take three to four weeks to complete. Allowing about three to four days for LIFEPAC introduction, review, and tests, the student has approximately 15 days to complete the LIFEPAC pages. Simply take the number of pages in the LIFEPAC, divide it by 15 and you will have the number of pages that must be completed on a daily basis to keep the student on schedule. For example, a LIFEPAC containing 45 pages will require three completed pages per day. Again, this is only an average. While working a 45-page LIFEPAC, the student may complete only one page the first day if the text has a lot of activities or reports, but go on to complete five pages the next day.

Long-range planning requires some organization. Because the traditional school year originates in the early fall of one year and continues to late spring of the following year, a calendar should be devised that covers this period of time. Approximate beginning and completion dates can be noted on the calendar as well as special occasions such as holidays, vacations and birthdays. Since each LIFEPAC takes three to four weeks or 18 days to complete, it should take about 180 school days to finish a set of ten LIFEPACs. Starting at the beginning school date, mark off 18 school days on the calendar and that will become the targeted completion date for the first LIFEPAC. Continue marking the calendar until you have established dates for the remaining nine LIFEPACs making adjustments for previously noted holidays and vacations. If all five subjects are being used, the ten established target dates should be the same for the LIFEPACs in each subject.

TEACHING SUPPLEMENTS

The sample weekly lesson plan and student grading sheet forms are included in this section as teacher support materials and may be duplicated at the convenience of the teacher.

The student grading sheet is provided for those who desire to follow the suggested guidelines for assignment of letter grades as previously discussed. The student's self test scores should be posted as percentage grades. When the LIFEPAC is completed, the teacher should average the self test grades, multiply the average by .25 and post the points in the box marked self test points. The LIFEPAC percentage grade should be multiplied by .60 and posted. Next, the teacher should award and post points for written reports and oral work. A report may be any type of written work assigned to the student whether it is a LIFEPAC or additional learning activity. Oral work includes the student's ability to respond orally to questions which may or may not be related to LIFEPAC activities or any type of oral report assigned by the teacher. The points may then be totaled and a final grade entered along with the date that the LIFEPAC was completed.

The Student Record Book, which was specifically designed for use with the Alpha Omega curriculum, provides space to record weekly progress for one student over a nine-week period as well as a place to post self test and LIFEPAC scores. The Student Record Books are available through the current Alpha Omega catalog; however, unlike the enclosed forms, these books are not for duplication and should be purchased in sets of four to cover a full academic year.

WEEKLY LESSON PLANNER

Week of:

	Subject	Subject	Subject	Subject
Monday				
Tuesday				
Wednesday				
Thursday				
Friday				

WEEKLY LESSON PLANNER

Week of:

	Subject	Subject	Subject	Subject
Monday				
Tuesday				
Wednesday				
Thursday				
Friday				

Student Name _____   Year _____

Bible

LP	Self Test Scores by Sections					Self Test Points	LIFEPAC Test	Oral Points	Report Points	Final Grade	Date
	1	2	3	4	5						
01											
02											
03											
04											
05											
06											
07											
08											
09											
10											

History & Geography

LP	Self Test Scores by Sections					Self Test Points	LIFEPAC Test	Oral Points	Report Points	Final Grade	Date
	1	2	3	4	5						
01											
02											
03											
04											
05											
06											
07											
08											
09											
10											

Language Arts

LP	Self Test Scores by Sections					Self Test Points	LIFEPAC Test	Oral Points	Report Points	Final Grade	Date
	1	2	3	4	5						
01											
02											
03											
04											
05											
06											
07											
08											
09											
10											

Student Name _____   Year _____

Math

LP	Self Test Scores by Sections 1	2	3	4	5	Self Test Points	LIFEPAC Test	Oral Points	Report Points	Final Grade	Date
01											
02											
03											
04											
05											
06											
07											
08											
09											
10											

Science

LP	Self Test Scores by Sections 1	2	3	4	5	Self Test Points	LIFEPAC Test	Oral Points	Report Points	Final Grade	Date
01											
02											
03											
04											
05											
06											
07											
08											
09											
10											

Spelling/Electives

LP	Self Test Scores by Sections 1	2	3	4	5	Self Test Points	LIFEPAC Test	Oral Points	Report Points	Final Grade	Date
01											
02											
03											
04											
05											
06											
07											
08											
09											
10											

INSTRUCTIONS FOR FIFTH GRADE MATH

The LIFEPAC curriculum from grades two through twelve is structured so that the daily instructional material is written directly into the LIFEPACs. The student is encouraged to read and follow this instructional material in order to develop independent study habits. The teacher should introduce the LIFEPAC to the student, set a required completion schedule, complete teacher checks, be available for questions regarding both content and procedures, administer and grade tests, and develop additional learning activities as desired. Teachers working with several students may schedule their time so that students are assigned to a quiet work activity when it is necessary to spend instructional time with one particular student.

Math is a subject that requires skill mastery. But skill mastery needs to be applied toward active student involvement. Measurements require measuring cups, rulers, empty containers. Boxes and other similar items help the study of solid shapes. Construction paper, beads, buttons, and beans are readily available and can be used for counting, base ten, fractions, sets, grouping, and sequencing. Students should be presented with problem situations and be given the opportunity to find their solutions.

Any workbook assignment that can be supported by a real-world experience will enhance the student's ability for problem solving. There is an infinite challenge for the teacher to provide a meaningful environment for the study of math. It is a subject that requires constant assessment of student progress. Do not leave the study of math in the classroom.

MATH 501

Unit 1: Place Value, Addition, and Subtraction

ANSWER KEYS

SECTION 1

1.1	a. 2				
	b. 4				
	c. 6				
	d. 3				
	e. 1				
	f. 5				

1.2 b

1.3 d

1.4 c

1.5 a

1.6 b

1.7 d

1.8 Answers will vary. Students should write a number that has a 7 in the thousands place. One example is 87,000.

1.9 a

1.10 d

1.11 c

1.12 b

1.13 eight million, four hundred nine thousand, one hundred twenty

Students should use commas correctly and not use the word *and*.

1.14 a

1.15 c

1.16 d

1.17 d

1.18 a. 2

b. 1

1.19 a

1.20 a

1.21 b

1.22 b

1.23 c

1.24 a

1.25 d

1.26 c

1.27 b

Earth is 149,598,262 kilometers from the Sun, and Venus is 108,209,475 kilometers from the Sun. So, Earth is farther from the Sun than Venus.

1.28	4,506	4,522	4,690	4,692
1.29	945,230	1,249,000	1,853,100	50,489,200

1.30 a. 2

b. 1

c. 4

d. 3

1.31 a. 4

b. 2

c. 3

d. 5

e. 1

1.32 true

1.33 d

1.34 a

1.35 b

1.36 d

1.37 d

1.38 c

1.39 a

1.40 c

1.41 b

1.42 a

1.43 d

1.44 b

1.45 a

1.46 a

1.47 b

1.48 c

1.49 greater, larger, larger in value, etc.

1.50 c

1.51 c

1.52	0.004	0.04	0.044	0.404
1.53	5.07	5.2	6.035	6.305
1.54	10.08	10.175	10.5	10.54

1.55 b

1.56 c

1.57 a

1.58 a

1.59 b

1.60 b

1.61 a

1.62 d

1.63	0.45	0.7	0.963	
1.64	2.008	2.08	2.8	
1.65	5.899	15.2	50.76	150.0
1.66	9.15	9.3	9.376	9.51

SELF TEST 1

1.01 false

> Whole numbers do not use the word *and*.

1.02 true
1.03 ten thousands
1.04 c
1.05 d
1.06 a
1.07 b
1.08 a
1.09 b
1.010 b
1.011 c
1.012 232,407   232,411   235,116   235,305
1.013 5.0   5.008   5.15
1.014 9
1.015 3

SECTION 2

2.1 rounding
2.2 c

> The digit to the right of the hundreds place (7) is greater than 5, so round 5 up to 6.

2.3 b

> The digit to the right of the millions place (9) is greater than 5, so round 8 up to 9.

2.4 a

> 7 is in the hundreds place. The digit to the right of the hundreds place (0) is less than 5, so keep 7 the same.

2.5 d

> 0 is in the tens place. The digit to the right of the tens place (3) is less than 5, so keep 0 the same.

2.6 c

> 9 is in the thousands place. The digit to the right of the thousands place is greater than 5, so round 9 up to 10.

2.7 b

> The digit to the right of the tenths place (7) is greater than 5, so round 3 up to 4.

2.8 d

> The digit to the right of the hundredths place (2) is less than 5, so keep 9 the same.

2.9 b

> 8 is in the ones place. The digit to the right of the ones place (5) is 5 so round 8 up to 9.

2.10 b

> 9 is in the tenths place. The digit to the right of the tenths place (7) is greater than 5, so round 9 up to 10.

2.11   a

> 3 is in the hundredths place. The digit to the right of the hundredths place (1) is less than 5, so keep 3 the same.

2.12   Answers will vary. The number should be a whole number between 650 and 749.

2.13   Answers will vary. The number should be a decimal number between 0.250 and 0.349.

2.14   a

2.15   b

2.16   c

2.17   d

2.18   a. 3
         b. 2
         c. 1

2.19   false

> The largest place value they share is the tens place.

2.20   true

2.21   b

2.22   c

> 1,000 + 9,000 = 10,000

2.23   d

> 180 – 60 = 120

2.24   a

> 22 + 4 + 2 = 28

2.25   c

> 6 – 1 = 5

2.26   b

> 700 + 600 = 1,300

2.27   a

> 700 – 600 = 100

2.28   c

> $10 + $10 + $20 = $40

2.29   d

> 18 – 7 = 11

2.30   a. 2
         b. 4
         c. 3
         d. 1

2.31   a. 2
         b. 5
         c. 1
         d. 4
         e. 3

2.32   mental math, mental addition, etc.

2.33   c

2.34   b

2.35   a

2.36   c

2.37   93

> 28 + 60 = 88
> 88 + 5 = 93

2.38   77

> 14 + 6 = 20
> 20 + 57 = 77

2.39   290

> 80 + 40 = 120
> 120 + 100 = 220
> 220 + 70 = 290

2.40   682

> 432 + 200 = 632
> 632 + 50 = 682

2.41   45

> 82 – 30 = 52
> 52 – 7 = 45

2.42   934

> 1,254 – 300 = 954
> 954 – 20 = 934

2.43   416

> 532 – 100 = 432
> 432 – 10 = 422
> 422 – 6 = 416

2.44   c

2.45   c

2.46   c

2.47   d

SELF TEST 2

2.01 false

> The largest place value they have in common is the ones place.

2.02 true

2.03 b

2.04 b

> The digit to the right of the hundreds place (2) is less than 5, so keep 9 the same. The digits to the right of the hundreds place become zeros.

2.05 a

> 1 is in the thousands place. The digit to the right of the thousands place (7) is greater than 5, so round 1 up to 2. The digits to the right of the thousands place become zeros.

2.06 b

> 4 is in the ones place. The digit to the right of the ones place (2) is less than 5, so keep 4 the same. The digits to the right of the ones place become zeros.

2.07 c

> The digit to the right of the hundreds place (6) is greater than 5, so round 9 up to 10. The 4 becomes 5 and the 9 becomes a zero. The digits to the right of the hundredths place become zeros.

2.08 b

> $5 + 9 = 14$

2.09 b

> $9,000 - 4,000 = 5,000$

2.010 a

> $130 + 60 = 190$

2.011 c

> $\$5 - \$2 = \$3$

2.012 c

2.013 76

> $49 + 20 = 69$
> $69 + 7 = 76$

2.014 275

> $40 + 15 = 55$
> $220 + 55 = 275$

2.015 273

> $578 - 300 = 278$
> $278 - 5 = 273$

SECTION 3

3.1   9,750

3.2   b

```
     1 1
     497
   + 184
     681
```

3.3   a

```
      1 1
    3,448
   +  680
    4,128
```

3.4   c

```
   1 1  2 1
   25,180
    5,144
  + 1,887
   32,211
```

3.5   114,782

```
     1      1
    59,466
  + 55,316
   114,782
```

3.6   d

```
       9 9
     7 10 10 10
     8,0̸0̸0̸
     -  452
     7,548
```

3.7   a

```
    5 11 8 12
    6,1̸9̸2̸
    - 5,737
       457
```

3.8   c

```
    28,478
  - 13,326
    15,152
```

3.9   28,650

```
       8 14
    59,4̸66
  - 30,816
    28,650
```

3.10   a. 6
           b. 2
           c. 5
           d. 4
           e. 3
           f. 1

3.11   a. 2
           b. 4
           c. 3
           d. 1

3.12   845

3.13   b

```
      1
     42.7
   + 11.4
     54.1
```

3.14   a

```
     1    1
    31.25
   + 9.38
    40.63
```

3.15   c

```
     0.29
  + 10.70
    10.99
```

3.16   d

```
      1
    16.24
  + 15.00
    31.24
```

3.17   c

3.18   a

```
      4.00
      6.41
    + 3.20
    ───────
     13.61
```

3.19   b

```
      1 1
     15.25
     13.80
    + 16.40
    ───────
     45.45
```

3.20   d

```
      2.25
    + 1.50
    ──────
      3.75
```

3.21   98.8

```
     93.0
    + 5.8
    ──────
     98.8
```

3.22   11.08

```
       1
      7.48
    + 3.60
    ──────
     11.08
```

3.23   b
3.24   a
3.25   c
3.26   c
3.27   c
3.28   62.2

```
     88.9
    − 26.7
    ──────
     62.2
```

3.29   5.26

```
      7 11
      8.17
    − 2.91
    ──────
      5.26
```

3.30   7.4

```
        11
     0  1 10
     12.0
    − 4.6
    ──────
      7.4
```

3.31   17.88

```
     37.88
    − 20.00
    ───────
     17.88
```

3.32   20.89

```
      6 12
     27.29
    − 6.40
    ───────
     20.89
```

3.33   b

```
         10
      2  0 14
      3.14
    − 2.65
    ──────
      0.49
```

3.34   c

```
    $3.14        $10.00
    + 2.65       − 5.79
    ──────       ───────
    $5.79         $4.21
```

3.35   a

```
       1 10
      7.20
    − 7.08
    ──────
      0.12
```

3.36   3.6
3.37   3.37
3.38   15.8
3.39   7.41
3.40   15.38
3.41   13.5
3.42   16.74
3.43   16.08
3.44   7.7

SELF TEST 3

3.01 false

> Round each number to the highest place value they have in common, the hundreds. 3,800 + 500 = 4,300

3.02 b

3.03 c

```
    1    1
    18,257
  + 39,361
    57,618
```

3.04 a

```
   5  12 1 14
    6,224
  - 5,615
      609
```

3.05 c

```
       1
    1,450
  + 1,250
    2,700
```

3.06 b

```
       5 12
    1,362
  - 1,046
      316
```

3.07 d

```
    6  15
    7.5
  - 2.6
    4.9
```

3.08 b

```
      1   1
    6.75
    7.10
  + 7.25
   21.10
```

3.09 c

```
    1   1
    $1.39
  + 1.85
    $3.24
```

3.010 a

```
        9
    4 10 10
    $5.00
  -  3.24
    $1.76
```

3.011 13.84

```
    8.14
  + 5.70
   13.84
```

3.012 23.35

```
     1
   14.00
  + 9.35
   23.35
```

3.013 12.66

```
   16.78
  - 4.12
   12.66
```

3.014 22.6

```
      11
    2 1 10
    32.0
  -  9.4
    22.6
```

SECTION 4

4.1 a. 3
      b. 8
      c. 6
      d. 7
      e. 11
      f. 10
      g. 4
      h. 15
      i. 14
      j. 17
      k. 1
      l. 2
      m. 9
      n. 5
      o. 12
      p. 16
      q. 13

4.2 c

4.3 d

4.4 b

4.5 d

4.6 b

The digit to the right of the tenths place (5) is 5 or larger, so round 9 up to 10.

4.7 b

$40 - 20 = 20$

4.8 a

$93 - 40 = 53$
$53 - 7 = 46$

4.9 c

$$\begin{array}{r} {}^{1}\\ 23.00 \\ +\ 18.35 \\ \hline 41.35 \end{array}$$

4.10 b

$$\begin{array}{r} {}^{9\ \ 9\ 9}\\ {}^{0\ 10\ 10\ 10\ 10}\\ 10,000 \\ -\ 6,128 \\ \hline 3,872 \end{array}$$

LIFEPAC TEST

1. true
2. false

   400 + 200 = 600

3. 54,900   535,728   535,740   536,312
4. ten millions
5. a
6. b
7. d

   ```
        5 10
     135.6̸0̸
   – 135.25
       0.35
   ```

8. a
9. c
10. b
11. d

   2 is in the ten thousands place. The digit to the right of it (4) is less than 5, so keep the 2 the same.

12. a
13. c

   ```
        2  2
     $0.99
     $0.79
   + $1.25
     $3.03
   ```

14. d

15. b

   ```
    5 12   8 11
    6̸7̸,0̸1̸9
   – 48,827
     14,092
   ```

16. a

   ```
    1 1    1
    62,919
   + 48,827
   111,746
   ```

17. 4.14

   3 is in the hundredths place. The digit to the right of it (9) is greater than 5, so round 3 up to 4.

18. 13.84

   ```
      4.30
   +  9.54
     13.84
   ```

19. 3.15

   ```
          9
    5 1̸0 10
    6̸.0̸0̸
   – 2.85
     3.15
   ```

20. 60

   90 – 30 = 60

ALTERNATE LIFEPAC TEST

1. false

> 4 is in the thousandths place.

2. true

> 700 – 600 = 100

3. 67,500   612,009   612,052   614,100
4. d
5. a
6. a
7. c

> $$\begin{array}{r} 138.8\overset{7\ 10}{\cancel{\cancel{0}}} \\ -\ 138.05 \\ \hline 0.75 \end{array}$$

8. b
9. d
10. a
11. d

> The 2 is in the thousands place. The digit
> to the right of it (4) is less than 5, so keep
> 2 the same.

12. c
13. a

> $$\begin{array}{r} \overset{2\ \ 2}{\ }\ \$1.45 \\ \$0.89 \\ +\ \$0.79 \\ \hline \$3.13 \end{array}$$

14. b

> 158 + 6 = 164

15. b

> $$\begin{array}{r} \overset{6\ \ 14\ 2\ 10}{6\cancel{7},\cancel{4}\cancel{3}\cancel{0}} \\ -\ 35,614 \\ \hline 31,816 \end{array}$$

16. a

> $$\begin{array}{r} \overset{1\ 1}{\ }\ 35,614 \\ +\ 67,430 \\ \hline 103,044 \end{array}$$

17. 15.7

> The 6 is in the tenths place. The digit
> to the right of it (8) is greater than 5, so
> round 6 up to 7.

18. 14.92

> $$\begin{array}{r} 6.50 \\ +\ 8.42 \\ \hline 14.92 \end{array}$$

19. 4.55

> $$\begin{array}{r} \overset{9}{\ }\ \overset{7\ 10\ 10}{8.\cancel{0}\cancel{0}} \\ -\ 3.45 \\ \hline 4.55 \end{array}$$

20. 80

> 20 + 60 = 80

MATH 501
ALTERNATE LIFEPAC TEST

NAME _____

DATE _____

SCORE _____

80
100

Each numbered question = 5 points

Answer *true* or *false*.

1. _____ In the number 6.814, 4 is in the hundredths place.

2. _____ Using rounding, a good estimate for 712 – 589 is 100.

Place these numbers in order from smallest to largest.

3. 612,052   614,100   612,009   67,500

_____   _____   _____   _____

Circle the correct letter and answer.

4. In the number 82,129,000,000, the digit 1 is in the _____ place.
   a. billions   b. ten billions   c. millions   d. hundred millions

5. Compare using <, >, or =.   915,000,000 _____ 2,140,000,000
   a. <   b. >   c. =

6. Bennett is 138.8 centimeters tall, Garrett is 138.45 centimeters tall, and Kayla is 138.05 centimeters tall. Who is the tallest?
   a. Bennett   b. Garrett   c. Kayla

7. Bennett is 138.8 centimeters tall, Garrett is 138.45 centimeters tall, and Kayla is 138.05 centimeters tall. What is the difference in height between Bennett and Kayla?
   a. 0.3 centimeters   b. 0.03 centimeters   c. 0.75 centimeters   d. 0.4 centimeters

8. Which whole number property is demonstrated here?   23 + 2 = 2 + 23
   a. Associative Property of Addition
   b. Commutative Property of Addition
   c. Identity Property of Addition

9. In word form, 4.02 is _____ .
    a. four and two tenths
    b. four hundred two
    c. four two tenths
    d. four and two hundredths

10. What is 8,205,000 in expanded form?
    a. 8,000,000 + 200,000 + 5,000
    b. 8,000,000 + 200,000 + 50,000
    c. 8,000 + 200 + 5
    d. 8,000,000 + 20,000 + 5,000

11. Round 452,489 to the nearest thousand.
    a. 453,000   b. 450,000   c. 500,000   d. 452,000

12. Martin is at a basketball game. The concession stand menu is shown here. Put the menu items in order from least expensive to most expensive.
    a. candy, soda, nachos, pizza
    b. soda, candy, pizza, nachos
    c. soda, candy, nachos, pizza
    d. candy, soda, pizza, nachos

ITEM	COST
Pizza	$1.45
Candy	$0.89
Nachos	$1.25
Soda	$0.79

13. Refer to the menu from Question 12. How much will it cost to buy pizza, candy, and soda?
    a. $3.13   b. $2.93   c. $3.59   d. $3.49

14. To find the sum of 58 and 106 in her head, Janie followed these steps:
    She added 58 to 100 and got 158. She then added 158 to 6 and got 162.
    Which statement is true?
    a. Janie's answer is wrong. She should have added 60 to 158.
    b. Janie's answer is wrong. She added 158 to 6 incorrectly.
    c. Janie's answer is wrong. She added 58 to 100 incorrectly.
    d. Janie's answer is right.

15. Marcus and Ryan are at an arcade. Marcus scored 35,614 points on a video game. Ryan scored 67,430 points on the same game. How many more points did Ryan score than Marcus?
    a. 32,224   b. 31,816   c. 31,824   d. 32,816

16. Marcus and Ryan are at an arcade. Marcus scored 35,614 points on a video game. Ryan scored 67,430 points on the same game. What was their combined score?
    a. 103,044 points   b. 102,044 points   c. 92,144 points   d. 93,144 points

Write the correct answer on the line.

17. Round 15.682 to the nearest tenth.   _____

18. Add.   6.5 + 8.42   _____

19. Subtract.   8 – 3.45   _____

20. Round each number to the nearest ten to estimate.   22.6 + 63.1   _____

MATH 502

Unit 2: Multiplying Whole Numbers and Decimals

ANSWER KEYS

SECTION 1

1.1   a. 2
          b. 4
          c. 1
          d. 3

1.2   28
1.3   54
1.4   18
1.5   36
1.6   35
1.7   24
1.8   24
1.9   110
1.10 55
1.11 addition
1.12 false

> There is no zero in the product of the front digits. The factors have a total of three zeros, so the product of 80 and 700 will have three zeros.

1.13 a

> Round each factor to the nearest ten.
> $30 \times 40 = 1,200$
> Since factors were only rounded down, the estimate is an underestimate.

1.14 b

> Round 178 to the nearest hundred.
> $7 \times 200 = 1,400$
> Since factors were only rounded up, the estimate is an overestimate.

1.15 c

> $500 \times 40 = 20,000$

1.16 a

> $100 \times 300 = 30,000$

1.17 b

> $8 \times 600 = 4,800$

1.18 d

> $40 \times 20 = 800$

1.19 4,200

> $70 \times 60 = 4,200$

1.20 270

> $3 \times 90 = 270$

1.21 35,000

> $50 \times 700 = 35,000$

1.22 d
1.23 a
1.24 b
1.25 a. 3
          b. 1
          c. 2

1.26 a. 4
          b. 1
          c. 2
          d. 3
          e. 5

1.27 b
1.28 true
1.29 a
1.30 false

> Multiplying a number by 1 does not change the value of the number.

1.31 0
1.32 d
1.33 c
1.34 a
1.35 d
1.36 c

> $8 \times (40 + 5)$
> $(8 \times 40) + (8 \times 5)$
> $320 + 40 = 360$

1.37 a. 3
b. 5
c. 1
d. 4
e. 2
1.38 b
1.39 c
1.40 a
1.41 c
1.42 c
1.43 a. 252

```
    36
 ×   7
   252
```

b. 3,508

```
   877
 ×   4
 3,508
```

c. 2,835

```
    63
 ×  45
   315
+2,520
 2,835
```

d. 4,060

```
    70
 ×  58
   560
+3,500
 4,060
```

e. 9,994

```
   526
 ×  19
 4,734
+5,260
 9,994
```

1.44 d
1.45 b
1.46 a

SELF TEST 1

1.01 false

If all factors are rounded up, then the estimate is an overestimate.

1.02 true
1.03 b

Any number multiplied by 1 is itself.

1.04 d
1.05 d

There are four zeros in the factors, so the product will have four zeros too.

1.06 b

10 × 200 = 2,000

1.07 a
1.08 c
1.09 a

```
   107
 ×  26
   642
+2,140
 2,782
```

1.010 c

```
   107
 ×  26
   642
+2,140
 2,782
```

1.011 b

```
   107
 ×  26
   642
+2,140
 2,782
```

1.012 4,500

90 × 50 = 4,500

1.013 4,277

$$
\begin{array}{r}
91 \\
\times \quad 47 \\
\hline
637 \\
3,640 \\
\hline
4,277
\end{array}
$$

1.014 18,000

$60 \times 300 = 18,000$

1.015 18,144

$$
\begin{array}{r}
324 \\
\times \quad 56 \\
\hline
1,944 \\
16,200 \\
\hline
18,144
\end{array}
$$

SECTION 2

2.1   a. 1
         b. 2
2.2   b
2.3   b
2.4   c
2.5   b
2.6   d
2.7   d

$3 \times 3 \times 3 \times 3 = 81$

2.8   a
2.9   c

$5 \times 5 \times 5 = 125$

2.10 b
2.11 b

$3^2 = 3 \times 3 = 9$
$2^3 = 2 \times 2 \times 2 = 8$

2.12 a

$5^2 = 5 \times 5 = 25$
$3^3 = 3 \times 3 \times 3 = 27$

2.13 c

$9^2 = 9 \times 9 = 81$
$3^4 = 3 \times 3 \times 3 \times 3 = 81$

2.14 a. 7
         b. 3
         c. 6
         d. 5
         e. 8
         f. 1
         g. 4
         h. 2
2.15 a. 2
         b. 3
         c. 1
         d. 4
         e. 5
2.16 power
2.17 a. 2
         b. 1
         c. 3
2.18 b

To multiply by 100, write two zeros at the end of the number.

2.19 c

To multiply by 10, write one zero at the end of the number.

2.20 d

To multiply by 1,000, write three zeros at the end of the number.

2.21 d

$45 \times 100 = 4,500$

2.22 a

$561 \times 10^3 = 561,000$

2.23 b

$4 \times 10^2 = 400$
$9 \times 10 = 90$

2.24 a

$23 \times 10^3 = 23,000$
$250 \times 10^2 = 25,000$

2.25 c

$100 \times 144 = 14,400$

2.26 11,000

To multiply by 1,000, write three zeros at the end of the number.

2.27 45,000

To multiply by 100, write two zeros at the end of the number.

2.28 3,760

To multiply by 10, write one zero at the end of the number.

2.29 a
2.30 b
2.31 a
2.32 c
2.33 false
2.34 53,800
2.35 three

2.36 b

The decimal point moved two places to the right. So, he multiplied by 100.

2.37 a

The decimal point moved one place to the right. So, she multiplied by 10.

2.38 c

To multiply by 1,000, move the decimal point three places to the right.

2.39 d

Move the decimal point one place to the right.

2.40 a

Move the decimal point two places to the right.

2.41 b

Move the decimal point three places to the right.

2.42 c

Move the decimal point one place to the right.

2.43 d

Move the decimal point two places to the right.

2.44 b

Move the decimal point three places to the right.

2.45 a. 4
b. 9
c. 8
d. 2
e. 5
f. 10
g. 1
h. 3
i. 6
j. 7

SELF TEST 2

2.01   false

$7 \times 7 \times 7 = 7^3$

2.02   true

2.03   b

2.04   c

2.05   d

To multiply by 100, write two zeros at the end of the number.

2.06   c

To multiply by 10, write one zero at the end of the number.

2.07   b

2.08   c

2.09   b

$8 \times 10^3 = 8,000$
$9 \times 100 = 900$

2.010   a

The decimal point moved one place to the right, so it was multiplied by 10.

2.011   d

Move the decimal point three places to the right.

2.012   c

Move the decimal point two places to the right.

2.013   a

$7^2 = 7 \times 7 = 49$
$2^6 = 2 \times 2 \times 2 \times 2 \times 2 \times 2 = 64$

2.014   16

$2 \times 2 \times 2 \times 2 = 16$

2.015   180.4

Move the decimal point one place to the right.

SECTION 3

3.1   a. 3
         b. 5
         c. 4
         d. 9
         e. 1
         f. 6
         g. 8
         h. 7
         i. 2

3.2   a

3.3   c

3.4   a

$11 \times 5 = 55$

3.5   a

11.45 was rounded down, so the estimate is an underestimate.

3.6   d

$8 \times 10 = 80$

3.7   b

9.82 was rounded up, so the estimate is an overestimate.

3.8   c

$22 \times 5 = 110$

3.9   a

$6 \times \$2 = \$12$
$2.19 was rounded down, so the estimate is an underestimate.

3.10   a

$14 \times 5 = 70$

3.11   a

Rounding: $99 \times 2 = 198$
Power of ten: $100 \times 2.4 = 240$

3.12   b

$100 \times 56.379 = 5,637.9$

3.13 b

3.14 a

3.15 d

3.16 d

3.17 55, rounding, overestimate
48.5, power of ten, underestimate

11 × 5 = 55
10 × 4.85 = 48.5

3.18 c

3.19 a

3.20 d

3.21 b

3.22 c

```
      6.41
  ×     11
       641
      6410
     70.51
```

3.23 c

```
     19.6
  ×   300
   5,880.0
```

3.24 b

```
      81.5
  ×     28
      6520
     16300
    2,282.0
```

3.25 34.8

```
     2
      8.7
  ×     4
     34.8
```

3.26 48.06

```
    3 3
     5.34
  ×     9
    48.06
```

3.27 108.12

```
      2 4
      6.36
  ×     17
      4452
      6360
    108.12
```

3.28 c

3.29 d

3.30 b

3.31 d

3.32 grid

3.33 c

3.34 d

3.35 b

3.36 b

There are three decimal places in the factors, so there should be three decimal places in the product.

3.37 61.92

```
      2
      4 1
     17.2
  ×    3.6
     1022
     5160
    61.92
```

3.38 2.436

```
       2
       2
       5
      0.07
  ×   34.8
      056
     0280
     2100
    2.436
```

3.39 8.032

```
     12.55
  ×   0.64
      5020
     75300
    8.0320
```

3.40 47.022

```
      9.22
   ×   5.1
      922
    46100
   47.022
```

3.41 a. 2
b. 1
c. 6
d. 4
e. 3
f. 5

3.42 b

3.43 50.04 pounds

```
    2 2
    8.34
   ×   6
   50.04
```

3.44 $3.52

```
     2.20
   ×  1.6
     1320
     2200
     3.520
```

3.45 875 square feet

```
     350
   ×  2.5
    1750
    7000
   875.0
```

3.46 $37.35

Total yards: 2.25 yards × 4 dresses

```
    1 2
    2.25
   ×   4
    9.00
```

Total cost: 9 yards × $4.15

```
    1 4
    4.15
   ×   9
   37.35
```

The total cost for fabric is $37.35.

3.47 $21.64

Cost of earrings: 3 earrings × $6.38

```
    1 2
    6.38
   ×   3
   19.14
```

Total cost: $19.14 + $2.50

```
    19.14
   + 2.50
   21.64
```

The total cost for the earrings is $21.64.

3.48 $1.25

Cost of hot dogs: 5 hot dogs × $1.75

```
    3 2
    1.75
   ×   5
    8.75
```

Total cost: $10.00 – $8.75

```
     9 9
    10 10
   10.00
   − 8.75
    1.25
```

Mr. Townsend will receive $1.25 back in change.

3.49 a. Read the problem carefully.
b. Identify what you're trying to find.
c. Make a plan.
d. Solve the problem.
e. Check that your answer makes sense.

SELF TEST 3

3.01 true

3.02 b

3.03 c

3.04 c

$$8 \times 6 = 48$$

3.05 a

$$\begin{array}{r} 8.24 \\ \times\ 5.88 \\ \hline 6592 \\ 65920 \\ 412000 \\ \hline 48.4512 \end{array}$$

3.06 b

$$52.6 \times 10 = 526$$

3.07 d

$$\begin{array}{r} {}^{2\ 5} \\ 52.6 \\ \times\ \ \ 9 \\ \hline 473.4 \end{array}$$

3.08 d

3.09 c

$$2 \times 24 = 48$$

3.010 a

$$\begin{array}{r} 24 \\ \times\ 1.8 \\ \hline 192 \\ 240 \\ \hline 43.2 \end{array}$$

3.011 a

He rounded both numbers down, so the estimate is an underestimate.

3.012 d

$$\begin{array}{r} 3.75 \\ \times\ \ 2.5 \\ \hline 1875 \\ 7500 \\ \hline 9.375 \end{array}$$

3.013 b

Hourly fee: $5 \times \$1.50 = \$7.50$

$$\begin{array}{r} {}^{2} \\ 1.50 \\ \times\ \ \ 5 \\ \hline 7.50 \end{array}$$

Total cost: $\$7.50 + \$2.25$

$$\begin{array}{r} 7.50 \\ +\ 2.25 \\ \hline 9.75 \end{array}$$

The total cost to park for 5 hours is $9.75.

3.014 21.59

$$\begin{array}{r} 1.27 \\ \times\ \ 17 \\ \hline 889 \\ 1270 \\ \hline 21.59 \end{array}$$

3.015 28.985

$$\begin{array}{r} 3.41 \\ \times\ \ 8.5 \\ \hline 1705 \\ 27280 \\ \hline 28.985 \end{array}$$

SECTION 4

4.1   a. 10
        b. 7
        c. 9
        d. 3
        e. 11
        f. 13
        g. 1
        h. 12
        i. 6
        j. 4
        k. 8
        l. 5
        m. 2

4.2   c

$30 \times 500 = 15{,}000$

4.3   b

$7.38 \times 1{,}000 = 7{,}380$

4.4   b

The Commutative Property of Multiplication says that the order of the factors doesn't change the value of the product.

4.5   d
4.6   b

Multiplying by 10^2 is the same as multiplying by 100. So, write two zeros after 72, or 7,200.

4.7   c

To multiply by 10, move the decimal point one place to the right.

4.8   a

$$\begin{array}{r} 478 \\ \times\quad 32 \\ \hline 956 \\ 14{,}340 \\ \hline 15{,}296 \end{array}$$

4.9   d

$$\begin{array}{r} 984 \\ \times\quad 7.38 \\ \hline 7872 \\ 29520 \\ 688800 \\ \hline 7{,}261.92 \end{array}$$

4.10 a

$$\begin{array}{r} 47.50 \\ \times\quad 2.5 \\ \hline 23750 \\ 95000 \\ \hline 118.750 \end{array}$$

LIFEPAC TEST

1. true
2. false

> To multiply a decimal number by 10, move the decimal point one place to the right.

3. true
4. a. 3
   b. 2
   c. 1
   d. 4
5. b
6. c

> 20 × 200 = 4,000

7. b

> ```
>     234
>   ×  17
>   ─────
>    1638
>   2340
>   ─────
>   3,978
> ```

8. a

> $3^3 = 3 \times 3 \times 3 = 27$

9. d

> 4 × 12 = 48

10. c

> ```
>     11.9
>   ×  3.8
>   ──────
>    952
>   3570
>   ──────
>   45.22
> ```

11. b

> 10 × 43.27 = 432.7

12. b
13. b

> $100 = 10 \times 10 = 10^2$

14. c

> To multiply a whole number by 1,000, write three zeros at the end of the number.

15. a
16. d

> ```
>     1 3
>    8.15
>  ×    7
>  ──────
>   57.05
> ```

17. a

> Cost for three shirts: 3 × $7.99 = $23.97
> ```
>    2 2
>   7.99
>  ×   3
>  ─────
>  23.97
> ```
> Total cost: $23.97 + $12.00 = $35.97
> ```
>   23.97
> + 12.00
> ───────
>   35.97
> ```

18. 1,638

> ```
>      42
>  ×   39
>  ──────
>    378
>   1260
>  ──────
>  1,638
> ```

19. 942.6

> Move the decimal point two places to the right.

20. 154.1

> ```
>     23
>  ×  6.7
>  ──────
>    161
>   1380
>  ──────
>  154.1
> ```

ALTERNATE LIFEPAC TEST

1. false

   The exponent is 3.

2. true
3. false

   There will be three decimal places in the product.

4. a. 4
   b. 3
   c. 2
   d. 1
5. a
6. d

   20 × 300 = 6,000

7. a

   ```
     287
   ×  18
   ─────
    2296
    2870
   ─────
    5,166
   ```

8. c

   $2^3 = 2 \times 2 \times 2 = 8$

9. d

   8 × 11 = 88

10. b

    ```
      11.4
    ×  7.8
    ──────
       912
      7980
    ──────
     88.92
    ```

11. a

    10 × 75.14 = 751.4

12. c
13. a

14. b

    To multiply a whole number by 100, write two zeros at the end of the number.

15. d

    Three groups of 15 squares are shaded for a total of 45 shaded squares.

16. c

    ```
      1 2
      7.35
    ×    5
    ──────
     36.75
    ```

17. b

    Cost for three shirts: 3 × $10.99 = $32.97

    ```
      2 2
     10.99
    ×    3
    ──────
     32.97
    ```

    Total cost: $32.97 + $14.00 = $46.97

    ```
     32.97
    + 14.00
    ──────
     46.97
    ```

18. 2,752

    ```
       64
    ×  43
    ─────
      192
     2560
    ─────
     2,752
    ```

19. 86.75

    Move the decimal point one place to the right.

20. 126.9

    ```
       27
    ×  4.7
    ─────
      189
     1080
    ─────
     126.9
    ```

MATH 502

ALTERNATE LIFEPAC TEST

NAME _____

DATE _____

SCORE _____

Each numbered question = 5 points.

Answer *true* or *false*.

1. _____ In 6^3, the exponent is 6.

2. _____ To multiply a decimal number by 10^3, move the decimal point three places to the right.

3. _____ In the product of 1.4 and 2.89, there will be two decimal places.

Match each property with its example.

4. a. _____ Commutative Property of Multiplication   1. $8 \times 0 = 0$

    b. _____ Associative Property of Multiplication   2. $1 \times 6 = 6$

    c. _____ Identity Property of Multiplication   3. $5 \times (8 \times 3) = (5 \times 8) \times 3$

    d. _____ Zero Property of Multiplication   4. $4 \times 11 = 11 \times 4$

Circle the correct letter and answer.

5. Jace estimated a product to be 900. The actual product is 892. His estimate is an
    _____ .
    a. overestimate   b. underestimate

6. Estimate the product of 18 and 287.
    a. 2,000   b. 3,000   c. 4,000   d. 6,000

7. Find the product of 18 and 287.
    a. 5,166   b. 4,516   c. 4,066   d. 2,583

8. Compare using <, >, or =. 2^3 ___ 8
    a. <   b. >   c. =

9. Estimate the product of 7.8 and 11.4 by rounding.
    a. 77   b. 84   c. 96   d. 88

10. Multiply.   7.8 × 11.4
    a. 78.92   b. 88.92   c. 171.0   d. 77.32

11. Estimate the following product using a power of ten.   10.8 × 75.14
    a. 751.4   b. 775   c. 7,514   d. 7,750

12. Which of the following number sentences is an example of the Distributive Property?
    a. 4 × (10 + 8) = (4 × 10) + 8   b. 4 × (10 + 8) = (4 + 10) × 8
    c. 4 × (10 + 8) = (4 × 10) + (4 × 8)   d. 4 × (10 + 8) = (4 × 10) + (8 × 10)

13. What is another way to represent 10?
    a. 10^1 b. 10^2 c. 10^3 d. 10^4

14. Find the product. $67 × 10^2$
    a. 670   b. 6,700   c. 67,000   d. 670,000

15. Which multiplication problem is represented by this grid?
    a. 0.3 × 0.5 = 0.15
    b. 0.15 × 0.3 = 0.45
    c. 5 × 0.3 = 0.45
    d. 3 × 0.15 = 0.45

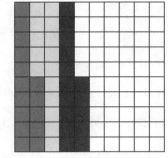

16. Jared makes $7.35 an hour working at a local sports equipment store. How much does he make in 5 hours?
    a. $12.35   b. $35.35   c. $36.75   d. $36.55

17. Mrs. Jensen bought a pair of shorts and three t-shirts. Each t-shirt cost $10.99, and the pair of shorts cost $14. What was her total cost?
    a. $24.99   b. $46.97   c. $52.99   d. $18.97

Fill in each blank with the correct answer.

18. 64 × 43 = _____

19. 10 × 8.675 = _____

20. 27 × 4.7 = _____

MATH 503

Unit 3: Dividing Whole Numbers and Decimals

ANSWER KEYS

SECTION 1

1.1   a. 2
       b. 1
       c. 4
       d. 3
1.2   a
1.3   c
1.4   a
1.5   a
1.6   12
1.7   3
1.8   5
1.9   9
1.10 6
1.11 7
1.12 $5 \times 6 = 30$ or $6 \times 5 = 30$
1.13 $3 \times 11 = 33$ or $11 \times 3 = 33$
1.14 a. 5
        b. 2
        c. 9
        d. 10
        e. 8
        f. 4
        g. 6
        h. 3
        i. 1
        j. 7
1.15 1
1.16 7
1.17 3
1.18 12
1.19 11
1.20 6
1.21 8
1.22 5
1.23 9
1.24 compatible numbers
1.25 b
1.26 c

$2,800 \div 7 = 400$

1.27 b

$4,000 \div 8 = 500$

1.28 a

$90 \div 3 = 30$

1.29 b

Mona changed the dividend to a larger number, so the estimate will be an overestimate.

1.30 b
1.31 a
1.32 b
1.33 b
1.34 d

630 is both compatible with 7 *and* close to 648.

1.35 b

$500 \div 5 = 100$

1.36 b

$3,600 \div 9 = 400$

1.37 500
1.38 70

$420 \div 6 = 70$

1.39 long division
1.40 d

630 is both compatible with 7 *and* close to 648.

1.41 a
1.42 c
1.43 b
1.44 49

```
              4 9
        6 ) 2 9 4
            2 4
              5 4
              5 4
                0
```

1.45   52

```
      5 2
  8 ) 4 1 6
      4 0
      1 6
      1 6
        0
```

1.46   347

```
      3 4 7
  2 ) 6 9 4
      6
      0 9
        8
        1 4
        1 4
          0
```

1.47   136

```
      1 3 6
  5 ) 6 8 0
      5
      1 8
      1 5
        3 0
        3 0
          0
```

1.48   584

```
        5 8 4
  7 ) 4,0 8 8
        3 5
        5 8
        5 6
          2 8
          2 8
            0
```

1.49   2,457

```
        2,4 5 7
  3 ) 7,3 7 1
        6
        1 3
        1 2
          1 7
          1 5
            2 1
            2 1
              0
```

1.50   b
1.51   d
1.52   a
1.53   d
1.54   d
1.55   a. Draw the long division sign and write
              in the dividend and divisor.
           b. Divide.
           c. Multiply.
           d. Subtract.
           e. Bring down the next digit in the dividend.
           f. Repeat the above steps until all digits in
               the dividend have been brought down.
1.56   remainder
1.57   a

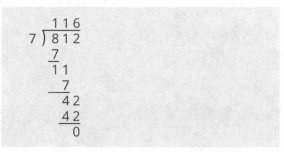

```
        1 1 6
  7 ) 8 1 2
      7
      1 1
        7
        4 2
        4 2
          0
```

1.58   d

```
        2 1    R 7
  8 ) 1 7 5
      1 6
        1 5
          8
          7
```

1.59   a
1.60   d
1.61   b
1.62   d
1.63   b

```
        1 6    R 1
  3 ) 4 9
      3
      1 9
      1 8
        1
```

1.64 c

```
        3 1 1   R 6
    9 ) 2,8 0 5
        2 7
        1 0
          9
          1 5
            9
            6
```

1.65 27 R1

```
         2 7   R 1
    3 ) 8 2
        6
        2 2
        2 1
          1
```

1.66 53 R6

```
         5 3   R 6
    8 ) 4 3 0
        4 0
        3 0
        2 4
          6
```

1.67 1,864 R2

```
        1,8 6 4   R 2
    5 ) 9,3 2 2
        5
        4 3
        4 0
          3 2
          3 0
            2 2
            2 0
              2
```

SELF TEST 1

1.01 false

> Multiply the quotient by the *divisor*.
> The product should be the *dividend*.

1.02 true
1.03 d
1.04 b

> 8**00** ÷ 4 = 2**00**

1.05 c

> 42**0** ÷ 6 = 7**0**

1.06 a

> 350 ÷ 5 = 70

1.07 d

```
         6 8
    5 ) 3 4 0
        3 0
        4 0
        4 0
          0
```

1.08 a

> 2,100 ÷ 7 = 300

1.09 b

```
        3 2 1   R 5
    7 ) 2,2 5 2
        2 1
        1 5
        1 4
          1 2
            7
            5
```

1.010 a

```
        2,1 8 4
    3 ) 6,5 5 2
        6
        0 5
          3
          2 5
          2 4
            1 2
            1 2
              0
```

1.011 b

```
        2 3     R 1
    4 ) 9 3
        8
        1 3
        1 2
          1
```

1.012 c

```
        7 6     R 7
    9 ) 6 9 1
        6 3
        6 1
        5 4
          7
```

1.013 12
1.014 8
1.015 4 × 6 = 24 or 6 × 4 = 24

SECTION 2

2.1   a. 9
          b. 10
          c. 8
          d. 1
          e. 3
          f. 7
          g. 5
          h. 6
          i. 4
          j. 2
2.2   multiple of ten
2.3   800
2.4   b, c, d, g
2.5   c
2.6   d
2.7   b
2.8   11

$$880 \div 10 = 88$$
$$88 \div 8 = 11$$

2.9   90

$$3,600 \div 10 = 360$$
$$360 \div 4 = 90$$

2.10 5

$$250 \div 10 = 25$$
$$25 \div 5 = 5$$

2.11 300

$$9,000 \div 10 = 900$$
$$900 \div 3 = 300$$

2.12 5

$$200 \div 10 = 20$$
$$20 \div 4 = 5$$

2.13 20

$$1,400 \div 10 = 140$$
$$140 \div 7 = 20$$

2.14 a. 2
          b. 1
          c. 4
          d. 5
          e. 3

2.15   Estimating
2.16   84

```
         8 4
  11 ) 9 2 4
        8 8
          4 4
          4 4
            0
```

2.17   23

```
           2 3
  42 ) 9 6 6
         8 4
         1 2 6
         1 2 6
             0
```

2.18   147

```
            1 4 7
  17 ) 2,4 9 9
          1 7
            7 9
            6 8
            1 1 9
            1 1 9
                0
```

2.19   36

```
             3 6
  53 ) 1,9 0 8
          1 5 9
            3 1 8
            3 1 8
                0
```

2.20   81

```
             8 1
  78 ) 6,3 1 8
          6 2 4
              7 8
              7 8
                0
```

2.21   306

```
            3 0 6
  14 ) 4,2 8 4
          4 2
            0 8 4
              8 4
                0
```

2.22   49

```
              4 9
  22 ) 1,0 7 8
          8 8
          1 9 8
          1 9 8
              0
```

2.23   b
2.24   b
2.25   a
2.26   a
2.27   d
2.28   divisor, dividend
2.29   64 R5

```
            6 4    R 5
  15 ) 9 6 5
         9 0
           6 5
           6 0
             5
```

2.30   13 R14

```
            1 3    R 14
  22 ) 3 0 0
         2 2
           8 0
           6 6
           1 4
```

2.31   204 R10

```
            2 0 4    R 10
  47 ) 9,5 9 8
         9 4
           1 9 8
           1 8 8
             1 0
```

2.32   37 R27

```
        37    R 27
88 ) 3,2 8 3
     2 6 4
       6 4 3
       6 1 6
          2 7
```

2.33   134 R42

```
        1 3 4    R 42
54 ) 7,2 7 8
     5 4
     1 8 7
     1 6 2
       2 5 8
       2 1 6
          4 2
```

2.34   Remainders
2.35   d
2.36   15
2.37   7
2.38   4
2.39   6
2.40   12
2.41   133
2.42   5
2.43   29
2.44   c
2.45   a
2.46   b

SELF TEST 2

2.01   true
2.02   false

> To divide a number by 50, first divide it by 10 and then divide the remaining amount by 5.

2.03   c

> 5,400 ÷ 10 = 540
> 540 ÷ 9 = 60

2.04   b

> 2,000 ÷ 40 = 50

2.05   a

```
          5 2
38 ) 1,9 7 6
     1 9 0
         7 6
         7 6
            0
```

2.06   d
2.07   c

```
       2 0 3    R 7
17 ) 3,4 5 8
     3 4
     0 5 8
       5 1
          7
```

2.08   a

```
        1 1    R 42
73 ) 8 4 5
     7 3
     1 1 5
       7 3
         4 2
```

2.09   c

> 149 ÷ 18 = 8 R5

2.010   d

> 149 ÷ 18 = 8 R5

2.011 a

2,000 ÷ 6 = 333 R2

2.012 b

2,000 ÷ 6 = 333 R2

2.013 27

```
        2 7
  24 ) 6 4 8
      4 8
      1 6 8
      1 6 8
          0
```

2.014 28 R14

```
        2 8    R 14
  37 ) 1,0 5 0
      7 4
      3 1 0
      2 9 6
        1 4
```

2.015 41

SECTION 3

3.1 zero
3.2 70
3.3 210
3.4 8
3.5 900
3.6 3
3.7 540
3.8 237
3.9 400
3.10 65
3.11 b

Move the decimal point one place to the left.

3.12 b

Move the decimal point two places to the left.

3.13 c

Move the decimal point three places to the left.

3.14 a

The decimal point was moved one place to the left, so 45 was divided by 10.

3.15 0.016

Move the decimal point three places to the left.

3.16 d

Move the decimal point two places to the left.

3.17 a

Move the decimal point one place to the left.

3.18 c

Move the decimal point three places to the left.

3.19 b

> The decimal point was moved two places to the left, so 517.23 was divided by 100.

3.20 0.97

> Move the decimal point one place to the left.

3.21 4.5185

> Move the decimal point two places to the left.

3.22
a. 3
b. 5
c. 1
d. 2
e. 4

3.23 c
3.24 c
3.25 b
3.26 a
3.27 a
3.28 1.48

```
        1.4 8
  7 ) 1 0.3 6
      7
      3 3
      2 8
        5 6
        5 6
          0
```

3.29 8.06

```
       8.0 6
 8 ) 6 4.4 8
     6 4
       0 4 8
         4 8
           0
```

3.30 9.5

```
        9.5
 4 ) 3 8.0
     3 6
       2 0
       2 0
         0
```

3.31 16.7

```
       1 6.7
 2 ) 3 3.4
     2
     1 3
     1 2
       1 4
       1 4
         0
```

3.32 18.4

```
       1 8.4
 3 ) 5 5.2
     3
     2 5
     2 4
       1 2
       1 2
         0
```

3.33 a
3.34 c
3.35 a
3.36 d
3.37 b
3.38 a
3.39 c
3.40 Decimal
3.41 d
3.42 a

```
       0.1 4
 8 ) 1.1 2
     8
     3 2
     3 2
       0
```

3.43 c

```
       1.6 4
 5 ) 8.2 0
     5
     3 2
     3 0
       2 0
       2 0
         0
```

3.44 b

```
      1  1
    $3.75
  +  2.49
    $6.24
```

3.45 a

```
       3.1 2
   2 ) 6.2 4
       6
       0 2
         2
         0 4
           4
           0
```

3.46 d

```
        5 4.1 8
   3 ) 1 6 2.5 4
       1 5
         1 2
         1 2
           0 5
             3
             2 4
             2 4
               0
```

3.47 b

```
        3.2 5
   7 ) 2 2.7 5
       2 1
         1 7
         1 4
           3 5
           3 5
             0
```

31.50 ÷ 10 = 3.15

3.48 a

```
       1.7 3              1.7 8
   3 ) 5.1 9          5 ) 8.9 0
       3                  5
       2 1                3 9
       2 1                3 5
         0 9                4 0
           9                4 0
           0                  0
```

3.49 c

```
        1 4.0 8
   2 ) 2 8.1 6
       2
       0 8
         8
         0 1 6
           1 6
             0
```

3.50 a. Read the problem carefully.
        b. Identify what you're trying to find.
        c. Make a plan.
        d. Solve the problem.
        e. Check that your answer makes sense.

SELF TEST 3

3.01   false

> Move the decimal point one place
> to the left.

3.02   true

> $2.40 ÷ 10 = $0.24 per ounce
> $2.08 ÷ 8 = $0.26 per ounce

3.03   b

> Move the decimal point three places
> to the left.

3.04   a

> Move the decimal point one place
> to the left.

3.05   b

> The decimal point was moved two places
> to the left.

3.06   d
3.07   c
3.08   a

```
      2 7.6
   3 ) 8 2.8
      6
      2 2
      2 1
        1 8
        1 8
          0
```

3.09   b

```
       6 3.2
   8 ) 5 0 5.6
      4 8
       2 5
       2 4
         1 6
         1 6
           0
```

3.010   c

```
       1 8 8.6 0
   4 ) 7 5 4.4 0
      4
      3 5
      3 2
        3 4
        3 2
          2 4
          2 4
            0 0
```

3.011   c

```
         1
     $15.50
   +   3.74
    $19.24
```

3.012   d

```
        9.6 2
   2 ) 1 9.2 4
      1 8
      1 2
      1 2
        0 4
          4
          0
```

3.013   2.15

```
        2.1 5
   7 ) 1 5.0 5
      1 4
      1 0
        7
        3 5
        3 5
          0
```

3.014   8.491

> Move the decimal point three places
> to the left.

3.015   72.352

> Move the decimal point two places
> to the left.

SECTION 4

4.1   a. 8
           b. 1
           c. 6
           d. 5
           e. 4
           f. 7
           g. 3
           h. 2

4.2   b

$28 \div 4 = 7$

4.3   d

$2{,}400 \div 6 = 400$

4.4   a

$3{,}500 \div 10 = 350$
$350 \div 5 = 70$

4.5   c

The decimal point was moved three places to the left.

4.6   b

```
       3 8 6
   6 ) 2,3 1 6
       1 8
         5 1
         4 8
           3 6
           3 6
            0
```

4.7   c

```
          2 4
   57 ) 1,3 6 8
        1 1 4
          2 2 8
          2 2 8
             0
```

4.8   d

```
        4.3 7
   8 ) 3 4.9 6
       3 2
         2 9
         2 4
           5 6
           5 6
            0
```

4.9   d

```
        8 6    R 3
   4 ) 3 4 7
       3 2
         2 7
         2 4
           3
```

4.10   b

```
        1 4 2    R 12
   39 ) 5,5 5 0
        3 9
        1 6 5
        1 5 6
            9 0
            7 8
            1 2
```

4.11   a

```
         1.9 6
   3 ) 5.8 8
       3
       2 8
       2 7
         1 8
         1 8
          0
```

LIFEPAC TEST

1. true
2. false

```
        37   R 14
  56 ) 2,086
       168
        406
        392
         14
```

3. a
4. d

22 ÷ 4 = 5 R2

5. a

240 ÷ 10 = 24 and 24 ÷ 8 = 3

6. c

The dividend is 21, the divisor is 7, and the quotient is 3.

7. b

1,8**00** ÷ 3 = 6**00**

8. d

Move the decimal point three places to the left.

9. a

640 ÷ 8 = 80

10. d

```
        38   R 5
   6 ) 233
       18
        53
        48
         5
```

11. b

```
        645   R 3
   4 ) 2,583
       24
        18
        16
         23
         20
          3
```

12. b

140 ÷ 22 = 6 R8

13. c
14. a

```
         22   R 9
   27 ) 603
        54
         63
         54
          9
```

15. a

```
      1 1
   $8.97
 + 0.63
  $9.60
```

16. c

```
       3.2 0
   3 ) 9.6 0
       9
       0 6
         6
         0 0
```

17. 9

36 ÷ 9 = 4

18. 504

```
      5 0 4
13 ) 6,5 5 2
      6 5
      0 5 2
        5 2
         0
```

19. 94

```
       9 4
  8 ) 7 5 2
      7 2
      3 2
      3 2
       0
```

20. 4.68

```
       4.6 8
  3 ) 1 4.0 4
      1 2
      2 0
      1 8
        2 4
        2 4
         0
```

ALTERNATE LIFEPAC TEST

1. false

$630 \div 10 = 63$ and $63 \div 7 = 9$

2. true

```
        5 2    R 18
51 ) 2,6 7 0
     2 5 5
     1 2 0
     1 0 2
         1 8
```

3. c
4. c

$16 \div 3 = 5$ R1

5. b

$3,200 \div 10 = 320$ and $320 \div 4 = 80$

6. b

The dividend is 45, the divisor is 9, and the quotient is 5.

7. b
8. b

Move the decimal point two places to the left.

9. b

$1,200 \div 4 = 300$

10. b

```
      4 2    R 3
 6 ) 2 5 5
     2 4
     1 5
     1 2
      3
```

11.   c

```
      3 3 2   R 1
4 ) 1,3 2 9
    1 2
    1 2
      1 2
        0 9
          8
          1
```

12.   b

127 ÷ 24 = 5 R7

13.   d
14.   a

```
      2 3   R 9
26 ) 6 0 7
     5 2
     8 7
     7 8
       9
```

15.   b

```
       1
   $1 1.1 6
 +   0.6 8
   $1 1.8 4
```

16.   d

```
      2.9 6
4 ) 1 1.8 4
    8
    3 8
    3 6
      2 4
      2 4
        0
```

17.   8

56 ÷ 8 = 7

18.   403

```
        4 0 3
16 ) 6,4 4 8
     6 4
       0 4 8
         4 8
           0
```

19.   68

```
       6 8
7 ) 4 7 6
    4 2
    5 6
    5 6
      0
```

20.   3.37

```
        3.3 7
5 ) 1 6.8 5
    1 5
    1 8
    1 5
      3 5
      3 5
        0
```

MATH 503

ALTERNATE LIFEPAC TEST

NAME _____

DATE _____

SCORE _____

Each **numbered question** = 5 points

Answer _true_ or _false_.

1. _____ The quotient of 630 and 70 is 90.

2. _____ The quotient of 2,670 and 51 is 52 R18.

Circle the correct letter and answer.

3. To divide a whole number or decimal by 1,000, move the decimal point _____ place(s) to the left.
   a. one   b. two   c. three   d. four

4. At a carnival, it takes three tickets for each ride. Shannon has 16 tickets, so she can go on _____ rides.
   a. three   b. four   c. five   d. six

5. Find _n_.   3,200 ÷ 40 = _n_
   a. _n_ = 8   b. _n_ = 80   c. _n_ = 800

6. In 45 ÷ 9 = 5, the divisor is _____ .
   a. 45   b. 9   c. 5

7. Divide.   480 ÷ 6
   a. 800   b. 80   c. 8   d. 18

8. Divide.   2.18 ÷ 100
   a. 21.8   b. 0.0218   c. 0.218   d. 0.00218

9. Estimate the quotient using compatible numbers.   1,329 ÷ 4
   a. 30   b. 300   c. 40   d. 400

10. Find the quotient. What is the remainder?   255 ÷ 6
    a. 1   b. 3   c. 4   d. 5

11. Find the quotient.   1,329 ÷ 4
    a. 333 R3   b. 482 R1   c. 332 R1   d. 483 R3

12. A train car can hold 24 passengers. If there are 127 passengers, how many train cars will be needed to carry all of them?
    a. 5   b. 6   c. 7

13. Which division problem is modeled here?
    a. 0.84 ÷ 14 = 0.6
    b. 0.94 ÷ 14 = 0.6
    c. 0.94 ÷ 6 = 0.14
    d. 0.84 ÷ 6 = 0.14

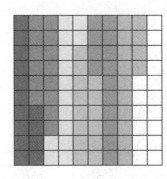

14. Divide.   607 ÷ 26
    a. 23 R9   b. 23 R11   c. 27 R5   d. 24 R17

15. Denise is buying four birthday cards for $11.16. Sales tax on the four cards is $0.68. What is the total cost?
    a. $11.74   b. $11.84   c. $10.48   d. $12.18

16. Denise is buying four birthday cards for $11.16. Sales tax on the four cards is $0.68. *Including* sales tax, what is the cost of each card?
    a. $2.88   b. $2.79   c. $3.47   d. $2.96

Write the correct answer on the line.

17. Find *n*.   56 ÷ *n* = 7   *n* = _____

Use long division to find the quotient.

18. 6,448 ÷ 16

19. 476 ÷ 7

20. 16.85 ÷ 5

MATH 504

Unit 4: Algebra and Graphing

ANSWER KEYS

SECTION 1

1.1   a. 2
        b. 1
        c. 4
        d. 3
        e. 5

1.2   d

$12 - 7 = 5$

1.3   d

Sue starts with 14 pencils, and some are taken away.

1.4   b

For each value of the variable, there is one solution.

1.5   c

$8 + 9 = 17$

1.6   b

$2 + 3 = 5$

1.7   a

She starts with 53 stamps and adds an unknown amount.

1.8   a

$23 - 8 = 15$

1.9   a

$5 - 4 = 1$

1.10 a. 4
        b. 1
        c. 3
        d. 5
        e. 2

1.11 Variables

1.12 c

$7 \times 11 = 77$

1.13 a

The amount of $20 is deposited d number of times.

1.14 b

For each value of the variable, there is one solution.

1.15 c

$9 \times 5 = 45$

1.16 d

$9 \times 3 = 27$

1.17 b

There are 6 rows, each with r roses.

1.18 c

$21 \times 4 = 84$

1.19 d

$6 \times 9 = 54$

1.20 a. 2
        b. 3
        c. 1
        d. 4
        e. 5

1.21 order of operations

1.22 c

Subtraction would not necessarily be the first operation, unless it were in parentheses.

1.23 a

$8 - 3 \times 2 + 5 =$
$8 - 6 + 5 =$
$2 + 5 = 7$

1.24 b

Parentheses are always evaluated first.

1.25 a

$5 \times (4 + 8 - 3) =$
$5 \times (12 - 3) =$
$5 \times (9) = 45$

1.26 c

$9 + (7 - 4)^2 \div 3 =$
$9 + 3^2 \div 3 =$
$9 + 9 \div 3 =$
$9 + 3 = 12$

1.27 b

$12 - (2 + 2)^2 \div 8 =$
$12 - 4^2 \div 8 =$
$12 - 16 \div 8 =$
$12 - 2 = 10$

1.28 b

Multiplication and division are first among the 4 basic operations. Division occurs first in this expression.

1.29 c

$2 + 2^3 \times 5 - 3 =$
$2 + 8 \times 5 - 3 =$
$2 + 40 - 3 =$
$42 - 3 = 39$

1.30
a. $4 + 4^2 \times 3 - 4$
b. $4 + 16 \times 3 - 4$
c. $4 + 48 - 4$
d. $52 - 4$
e. 48

1.31
a. $10 - 4 \times 2 + 2^2$
b. $10 - 4 \times 2 + 4$
c. $10 - 8 + 4$
d. $2 + 4$
e. 6

1.32
a. $12 + 4 \times 2 - 2^3$
b. $12 + 4 \times 2 - 8$
c. $12 + 8 - 8$
d. $20 - 8$
e. 12

SELF TEST 1

1.01 d

$8 + 5 = 13$

1.02 d

$7 + 5 = 12$

1.03 c

She starts with 16 coins and some are taken away.

1.04 b

$9 - 9 = 0$

1.05 a

$15 - 9 = 6$

1.06 c

$7 \times 8 = 56$

1.07 c

$9 \times 4 = 36$

1.08 a

The number of members is multiplied by 5 ($5 per member).

1.09 d

$4 \times 4 = 16$

1.010 c

$3 \times 7 = 21$

1.011 a

$12 - 3 \times 3 - 2 =$
$12 - 9 - 2 =$
$3 - 2 = 1$

1.012 c

$3 + 9 \div (9 - 6) =$
$3 + 9 \div 3 =$
$3 + 3 = 6$

1.013 a
1.014 b

$5 + 3 \times (5 - 2)^2 =$
$5 + 3 \times (3)^2 =$
$5 + 3 \times 9 =$
$5 + 27 = 32$

1.015 d

$4 + 4^2 - 5 \times 2 =$
$4 + 16 - 5 \times 2 =$
$4 + 16 - 10 =$
$20 - 10 = 10$
(Although adding parentheses around 5×2 will produce a result of 10, it is not necessary.)

SECTION 2

2.1   equation

2.2   a

1 + 3 = 4

2.3   b

There is only one solution for an equation.

2.4   c

3 + 8 = 11

2.5   a

17 − 8 = 9

2.6   c

9 − 3 ≠ 12

2.7   b

The jar starts with 6 cookies and an unknown amount is added (+ x), giving a total of 15 cookies (= 15).

2.8   b

13 − x = 3, 13 − 10 = 3

2.9   d

Ms. Green starts with 18 pencils and an unknown amount is removed (− x), leaving 6 (= 6).

2.10   a. 6
b. 4
c. 8
d. 3
e. 1
f. 7
g. 5
h. 2

2.11   a variable

2.12   d

3 × 9 = 27

2.13   b

Only one number can be multiplied by 7 to get a product of 49 (7).

2.14   c

9 × 7 = 63

2.15   b

8 × 1 = 8

2.16   d

4 × 5 ≠ 25

2.17   c

11 × 13 = 143. Although students might not know mentally that 11 × 13 = 143, they should know that 11 × 9 = 99, 11 × 10 = 110, and that 11 × 20 is more than 200.

2.18   a

The variable is the number of people, and each person scores 4 points (4p), for a total of 28 (= 28).

2.19   c

10 × 9 = 90

2.20   a. 5
b. 1
c. 3
d. 8
e. 7
f. 2
g. 4
h. 6

2.21   a. 2
b. 1
c. 4
d. 3

2.22   b

y = 4 + 9, y = 13

2.23 c

The input can be any number.

2.24 b

If $x = 3$, $y = 2(3)$, so $y = 6$.

2.25 c

$14 = 8 + 6$

2.26 c

$y = 9 \times 5$, so $y = 45$.

2.27 d

$10 \neq 5 - 5$

2.28 c

$6 \neq 8 - 5$

2.29 b

$6 = 2 \times 3$, $8 = 2 \times 4$

2.30   a. 3
        b. 4
        c. 1
        d. 5
        e. 2

SELF TEST 2

2.01 b

$8 + 4 = 12$

2.02 a

The party starts with 3 people, and then an unknown number arrive (+ x), giving a total of 14 people (= 14).

2.03 c

$12 - 3 \neq 15$

2.04 b

$16 - x = 3$, so $x = 13$.

2.05 d

$13 - 8 = 5$

2.06 d

$9 \times 6 = 54$

2.07 c

$7 \times 10 = 70$

2.08 b

The variable is the number of tickets, at $10 each (10$t$), for a total of $90 (= 90).

2.09 c

$5 \times 4 \neq 54$

2.010 a

$3x = 24$, so $x = 8$.

2.011 b

$y = 3 + 4$, so $y = 7$.

2.012 a

$8 \neq 12 - 5$

2.013 b

> If $x = 3$, then $y = 4 \times 3$, so $y = 12$.

2.014 b

> $8 = 6 + 2$, $12 = 6 + 6$

2.015 d

> $12 \neq 2 - 10$

SECTION 3

3.1   a. 5
        b. 4
        c. 6
        d. 3
        e. 1
        f. 2

3.2   a

> 1 to the right, 9 up

3.3   c

> 5 to the right, 3 up

3.4   d

> 7 to the right, 0 up

3.5   a

> 5 to the right, 8 up

3.6   b

> The point is 9 to the right and 9 up.

3.7   b

> The point is 2 to the right and 6 up.

3.8   d

> The point is 3 to the right and 3 up.

3.9   c

> The point is 0 to the right and 2 up.

3.10   b

> The origin is the start of each axis, 0 in each direction.

3.11

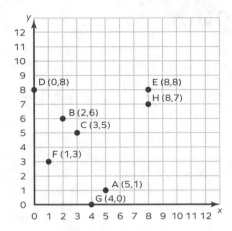

3.20

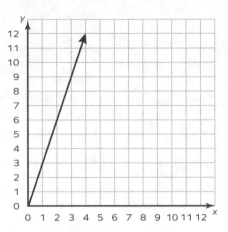

3.12 c

If $x = 7$, then $y = 5$: $y = 7 - 2$, $y = 5$.

3.13 d

If $x = 10$, then $y = 15$: $y = 10 + 5$, $y = 15$.

3.14 c

All of the functions students are working with are linear.

3.15 a

Line A passes through (0, 6): $6 = 0 + 6$.

3.16 c

If $x = 0$, then $y = 0$: $0 = 8 \times 0$.

3.17 b

If $x = 0$, then $y = 7$: $7 = 0 + 7$.

3.18 c, d

The lines are not the same steepness, and therefore not parallel.

3.19 a, c

If $x = 3$, then $y = 6$ for $y = x + 3$: $6 = 3 + 3$, and $y = 2x$: $6 = 2 \times 3$.

3.21 coordinate

3.22 a, c

1 gallon costs $3 and the cost increases by $3 for each additional gallon.

3.23 d

In 8 hours she would ride 80 miles; 10 miles each hour.

3.24 a

Graph A shows that 1 yard costs $4 and 2 yards cost $8, or 4 more dollars.

3.25 b, c

In each case, 0 input gives 0 output. No time has passed if she hasn't started running, and there is no cost if no gas is bought. In the other two cases, there is a starting number: 68° at 0 time, $5.00 at 0 minutes.

3.26 c

At 7 miles each hour, he'll run 7 × 8, or 56 miles.

3.27 b

At 6 miles each hour, he'll run 6 × 5, or 30 miles.

3.28   a, b, d

The graph begins at 3 miles (perhaps distance from home) and increases by 1 mile every 2 hours (or $\frac{1}{2}$ mile per hour).

3.29   a, d

Both graphs include the point located at (5, 4).

3.30   a. 5
b. 4
c. 2
d. 1
e. 3

3.31   a. 2
b. 6
c. 5
d. 3
e. 1
f. 4

3.32   b

10° is a positive temperature.

3.33   d

14°F is the only positive temperature.

3.34   c

Positive numbers are to the right of 0.

3.35   c

Fractions are between integers. Zero is an integer, although it is neither negative nor positive.

3.36   a, c

3 is 3 to the right of 0 and -3 is 3 to the left of 0.

3.37   c

The arrow is 7 units to the left of 0.

3.38   b

-2 is to the right of -7 on the number line, so it is larger.

3.39   a, b, c, d

The set of integers are positive and negative numbers and zero. Natural numbers are the same as positive numbers.

3.40   c

Moving left to right on the number line, -7, -4, -2, 1, and 5 are in order.

3.41   -8 -7 -3 2 8 9
3.42   6 3 0 -2 -6 -9

SELF TEST 3

3.01 a

The point is 0 to the right and 4 up.

3.02 d

The point is 9 to the right and 3 up.

3.03 d

The point is 8 to the right and 9 up.

3.04 b

The point is 4 to the right and 4 up.

3.05 d

Line D passes through (7, 0): 0 = 7 – 7.

3.06 c

If $x = 9$, then $y = 27$: $y = 3 \times 7$, $y = 21$.

3.07 a

If $x = 2$, then $y = 0$: $y = 2 + 2$, $y = 4$.

3.08 c, d

The lines are not the same steepness, so they are not parallel. They both rise up and to the right, starting from the origin.

3.09 a, b

1 minute costs 10 cents and the cost increases by 10 cents for each additional minute.

3.010 d

8 miles will take 56 minutes; 1 mile each 7 minutes: $8 \times 7 = 56$.

3.011 d

Each output is 4 more than its input; $10 + 4 = 14$.

3.012 d

Temperature above zero is positive.

3.013 d

All positive numbers are greater than all negative numbers.

3.014 c

Moving left to right on the number line, -2, -1, 0, 4, and 9 are in order.

3.015 a

The arrow is 4 units to the left of 0.

SECTION 4

4.1   b

$4 + 12 = 16$

4.2   b

$7 \times 8 = 56$

4.3   d

$10 + (8 - 4)^2 \div 2$
$10 + 4^2 \div 2$
$10 + 16 \div 2$
$10 + 8 = 18$

4.4   c

$8 - 5 = 3$

4.5   d

The variable is the number of people (p), and each person scores 6 points ($6p$), for a total of 42 (= 42).

4.6   a.   4
b.   7
c.   3
d.   8
e.   2
f.   1
g.   12
h.   10
i.   6
j.   13
k.   11
l.   9
m. 5

4.7   a.   13
b.   2
c.   6
d.   7
e.   10
f.   9
g.   8
h.   3
i.   5
j.   12
k.   4
l.   1
m. 11

4.8   d

$12 \neq 8 - 4$

4.9   c

The point is 8 to the right and 2 up.

4.10   b

The point is 5 to the right and 0 up.

4.11   a, d

If $x = 2$, then $y = 10$ for $y = x + 8$: $10 = 2 + 8$, and $y = 5x$: $10 = 5 \times 2$.

4.12   c

In 5 hours he would drive 1,000 miles; 200 miles each hour, or $200 \times 5 = 1,000$.

4.13   a, c

-6 is 6 to the left of 0 and 6 is 6 to the right of 0.

4.14   a

-6 is to the right of -8 on the number line, so it is larger.

LIFEPAC TEST

1. d

   $12 - 9 = 3$

2. b

   $4 + 2 = 6$

3. c

   $6 \times 3 = 18$

4. a

   $4 \times 9 = 36$

5. c

   $6 + 5 \times 3^2 - 8$
   $6 + 5 \times 9 - 8$
   $6 + 45 - 8$
   $51 - 8 = 43$

6. a

   Exponents come before the four basic operations.

7. a

   $9 - 6 \neq 4$

8. a

   $16 - 12 = 4$

9. d

   $2 \times 12 = 24$

10. b

    $3 \times 0 \neq 30$

11. b

    $6 = 12 - 6$

12. b

    $36 \neq 8 \times 4$

13. d

    7 to the right, 4 up

14. a

    The point is 9 to the right, and 7 up.

15. d

    If $x = 8$, then $y = 11$: $y = 8 + 3$, $y = 11$

16. a, b

    If $x = 4$, then $y = 12$ for $y = x + 8$: $12 = 4 + 8$, and $y = 3x$: $12 = 3 \times 4$.

17. c

    The plant is two inches more than the day number.

18. d

    In 5 hours, the car would travel 250 miles; $5 \times 50 = 250$.

19. d

    The plus sign indicates positive 8.

20. c

    Any positive number will be greater than any negative number.

ALTERNATE LIFEPAC TEST

1. b

    $3 + 4 = 7$

2. a

    $8 - 1 = 7$

3. b

    $9 \times 1 = 9$

4. c

    $8 \times 8 = 64$

5. b

    $10 - 4 \times 2 + 2$
    $10 - 8 + 2$
    $2 + 2 = 4$

6. b

    Parentheses are always evaluated first.

7. d

    $9 - 3 \neq 12$

8. b

    $7 + 3 = 10$

9. a

    $37 \times 0 = 0$

10. d

    $4 \times 7 \neq 24$

11. b

    $2 = 8 - 6$

12. a

    $7 \neq 6 - 1$

13. c

    The point is 8 to the right, and 5 up.

14. c

    The point is 3 to the right, and 4 up.

15. a

    If $x = 6$, then $y = 36$: $y = 6 \times 6$, $y = 36$

16. a, c

    If $x = 2$, then $y = 4$ for $y = x + 2$: $4 = 2 + 2$, and $y = 2x$: $4 = 2 \times 2$.

17. c

    At 10 miles each hour, he'll ride 10×8, or 80, miles.

18. a

    In 0 hours, the car would travel 0 miles; $0 \times 80 = 0$.

19. c

    Negative numbers are to the left of 0.

20. b

    Any positive number will be greater than any negative number.

MATH 504

ALTERNATE LIFEPAC TEST

NAME _____

DATE _____

SCORE _____

Each numbered question = 5 points.

Circle the correct letter and answer.

1. Evaluate the expression $x + 4$, if $x = 3$.
   a. 12   b. 7   c. 5   d. 1

2. Which expression has a solution of 7, if $r = 8$?
   a. $r - 1$ b. $r - 2$ c. $15 + r$ d. $r + 8$

3. Evaluate the expression $9x$, if $x = 1$.
   a. 8   b. 9   c. 10   d. 91

4. Which expression has a solution of 64, if $w = 8$?
   a. $6w$ b. $7w$ c. $8w$ d. $9w$

5. Evaluate the expression $10 - 4 \times 2 + 2$.
   a. 0   b. 4   c. 14   d. 24

6. What should be done first to evaluate the expression? $5 - 3 \times (4 - 2)^2 \div 5$
   a. Divide by 5   b. Subtract 2 from 4
   c. Subtract 3 from 5   d. Multiply by 3

7. For which equation is $s = 9$ *not* the solution?
   a. $3s = 27$ b. $s + 7 = 16$ c. $12 - s = 3$ d. $s - 3 = 12$

8. Find the value of x that makes this equation true: $7 + x = 10$
   a. $x = 2$ b. $x = 3$ c. $x = 17$ d. $x = 70$

9. Find the value of x that makes this equation true: $37x = 0$
   a. $x = 0$ b. $x = 1$ c. $x = 2$ d. $x = 3$

10. For which equation is $g = 7$ *not* the solution?
    a. $7g = 49$ b. $8 + g = 15$ c. $3g = 21$ d. $4g = 24$

11. Which ordered pair will be solution for the function $y = x - 6$?
    a. (7, 13)   b. (8, 2)   c. (9, 4)   d. (4, 10)

12. For the function shown in the table, which output is *incorrect*?
    a. A
    b. B
    c. C
    d. D

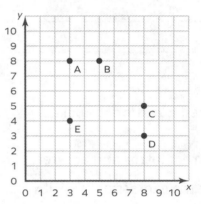

y = 6 – x		
x	y	
1	7	A
2	4	B
3	3	C
4	2	D

13. What point is located at (8, 5) on this graph?
    a. point A
    b. point B
    c. point C
    d. point D

14. What is the location of point E on the graph from Question 13?
    a. (4, 3)   b. (3, 3)
    c. (3, 4)   d. (4, 4)

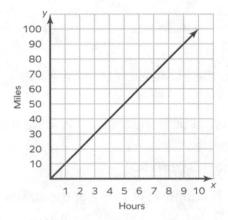

15. Which point is *not* on the graph of the function y = 6x?
    a. (6, 1)   b. (20, 120)   c. (7, 42)   d. (0, 0)

16. The graph of which function(s) will contain the point (2, 4)?
    a. y = x + 2   b. y = x – 2   c. y = 2x   d. y = 2 – x

17. If Don rides his bike 10 miles per hour, how far will he ride in 8 hours?
    a. 60 miles
    b. 70 miles
    c. 80 miles
    d. 90 miles

18. If Mario drives 80 miles per hour in his car, and this relationship is graphed, which ordered pair would *not* be on the graph?
    a. (0, 80)   b. (3, 240)   c. (6, 480)   d. (10, 800)

19. Which of the following is *not* the same as negative 5?
    a. 5 units to the left of 0 on a number line   b. -5
    c. 5 units to the right of 0 on a number line   d. the opposite of 5

20. Which comparison is *not* correct?
    a. -4 < 1   b. 3 > 4   c. -2 < 8   d. 3 > -7

MATH 505

Unit 5: Measurement

ANSWER KEYS

SECTION 1

1.1 a. 4
    b. 2
    c. 1
    d. 9
    e. 7
    f. 10
    g. 6
    h. 3
    i. 8
    j. 12
    k. 11
    l. 5

1.2 d

"deca-" means "ten," just as a decade is ten years

1.3 c

"hecto-" means "100"

1.4 a

m stands for milli- and meters

1.5 b

"kilo-" means "1,000"

1.6 d

The liter is the basic unit of capacity.

1.7 c

"milli-" means "$\frac{1}{1,000}$," so a millimeter is one thousandth of a meter

1.8 c

There are three zeros in 1,000, so the decimal moves 3 places to the right.

1.9 b

There two zeros in 100, so the decimal moves 2 places to the left.

1.10 b

1 kg = 1,000 grams. 1,000 mg are needed for just 1 g, and 10 dg are needed for 1 g.

1.11 a. 3
    b. 2
    c. 5
    d. 1
    e. 4

1.12 a. 3
    b. 1
    c. 2

1.13 c

10 meters is way too tall, and 75 cm and 980 mm are less than 1 meter.

1.14 c

A soccer field would be measured in yards, so meters are comparable.

1.15 a

A ladybug is about a centimeter long. 9 mm is the only measurement close to 1 centimeter.

1.16 d

The distance is comparable to miles (over 2,000 miles across the country), so kilometers are appropriate.

1.17 a

Divide to go from a smaller unit to a larger unit. Centimeters are 100 times smaller than meters so the decimal moves two places to the left.

1.18 d

Multiply to go from a larger unit to a smaller unit. Kilometers are 1,000 times larger than meters so the decimal moves three places to the right.

1.19   c

Each of the other choices is equivalent
to 5 m.
0.5 km = 500 m

1.20   b

80 centimeters is close to 1 meter
(100 cm = 1 m), as is 0.8 meters.
80 ÷ 100 = 0.8

1.21   a. 8
b. 4
c. 9
d. 6
e. 2
f. 5
g. 7
h. 3
i. 10
j. 1

1.22   a. 2
b. 1

1.23   c

80 kilograms is about 180 pounds.
Grams and milligrams are too small,
and 10 kilograms is only 22 pounds.

1.24   b

A car would be very heavy and would
be measured in kilograms.

1.25   c

630 g = 0.63 kg and is more than half a
kilogram (over 1 pound). Milligrams are
too small.

1.26   b

An apple would weigh less than 1 pound,
but 320 mg is way too small and 950 g is
nearly 1 kilogram (about 2 pounds).

1.27   a

Divide to go from a smaller unit to a larger
unit. Milligrams are 1,000 times smaller
than grams, so the decimal moves three
places to the left.

1.28   d

Multiply to go from a larger unit to a
smaller unit. Kilograms are 1,000 times
larger than grams so the decimal moves
three places to the right.

1.29   c

Each of the other choices is equivalent
to 6 g.
60 kg = 60,000 g

1.30   d

850 milligrams is close to 1 gram
(1,000 mg = 1 g), as is 0.850 g.
850 ÷ 1,000 = 0.850

1.31   a. 6
b. 4
c. 2
d. 9
e. 8
f. 1
g. 7
h. 10
i. 3
j. 5

1.32   c
1.33   b
1.34   a
1.35   a

A teaspoon would hold a small amount,
and 5 milliliters is by far the smallest
amount shown.

1.36   c

Only liters and milliliters are measures of
capacity and liters are 1,000 times larger
than milliliters.

1.37   c

A bowl holds less than 1 liter, and more
than 1 milliliter.

1.38   a

A coffee cup is about 12 ounces, well less
than a liter.

1.39   d

Divide to go from a smaller unit to a larger unit. Milliliters are 1,000 times smaller than liters, so the decimal moves three places to the left.

1.40   d

Multiply to go from a larger unit to a smaller unit. Liters are 1,000 times larger than milliliters so the decimal moves three places to the right.

1.41   c

$4.5 \times 1,000 = 4,500$

1.42   d

$85 \div 1,000 = 0.085$

1.43
a. 4
b. 9
c. 1
d. 6
e. 7
f. 10
g. 3
h. 5
i. 2
j. 8

SELF TEST 1

1.01   a

"hecto-" means "100"

1.02   a

A decameter is 10 meters. The other measures are a meter or less.

1.03   b

c stands for centi- and m stands for meters.

1.04   d

1256 m = 1.256 km

1.05   c

A football field is marked in yards, so meters are comparable.

1.06   a

A penny is close to 2 cm wide, and 19 mm = 1.9 cm.

1.07   d

$7.5 \times 1,000 = 7,500$

1.08   c

$3.4 \times 1,000 = 3,400$

1.09   a

Pills are measured in milligrams and are usually less than one gram.

1.010   a

A dime would weigh a few grams; 2.5 grams is 25 milligrams.

1.011   d

$3.2 \times 1,000 = 3,200$

1.012 c

$$5.7 \times 1,000 = 5,700$$

1.013 d

A quart is about 1 liter, so a half gallon is about 2 liters.

1.014 a

A teacup holds much less than a liter, but more than 6 milliliters.

1.015 d

$$7.8 \times 1,000 = 7,800$$

SECTION 2

2.1 Customary

2.2 c

A soccer field is too long to measure in feet, but is much less than a mile, so yards are appropriate.

2.3 a

A math book would be less than a foot wide but more than 2 inches.

2.4 b

4 feet = 48 inches.
4 feet, 2 inches = 50 inches.
50 – 14 = 36 inches.
36 inches = 3 feet.

2.5 d

$$34 \div 12 = 2 \text{ R}10$$

2.6 d

8 yards = 24 feet; 24 + 5 = 29 feet

2.7 d

$$9 \times 12 = 108$$

2.8 c

$\frac{1}{100}$ of a mile = 52.8 feet

2.9 a

1 yard = 3 feet; 5,280 feet = 1 mile.
5,280 ÷ 3 = 1,760

2.10   a. 4
    b. 5
    c. 2
    d. 7
    e. 8
    f. 3
    g. 1
    h. 6

2.11   c

2.12   a

> An adult would clearly be more than ounces and less than tons. Fifty pounds is closer to the weight of a small child.

2.13   b

> A baseball weighs less than 1 pound.

2.14   b, d

> An elephant would weigh more than a ton, but could still be listed by pounds.

2.15   c

> $96 \div 16 = 6$

2.16   b

> 4 tons = 8,000 lb.; 8,000 + 350 = 8,350

2.17   c

> 8 lb. = 128 oz. (8 × 16 = 128)

2.18   d

> 6 lb. = 96 oz. (6 × 16 = 96)
> 96 + 4 = 100

2.19   c

> 3 lb. = 2 lb. + 16 oz.; subtract 6 oz.:
> 2 lb. + 16 oz. – 6 oz. = 2 lb. + 10 oz.

2.20   a. 6
           b. 2
           c. 4
           d. 7
           e. 8
           f. 1
           g. 5
           h. 3

2.21   a

2.22   a

2.23   a

> A bucket would hold over one gallon, and only one choice is in gallons.

2.24   c

> For such a large quantity, only gallons would be used.

2.25   d

> A bowl holds more than 4 fluid ounces, and less than 1 quart.

2.26   a

> A coffee cup is less than 1 pint (16 fluid ounces).

2.27   b

> 4 quarts = 1 gallon; 12 ÷ 4 = 3

2.28   b

> 1 gallon = 8 pints; 8 × 4 = 32

2.29   c

> 32 fl. oz. = 1 quart = 4 cups = 2 pints

2.30   c

> 1 quart = 2 pints; 2 × 5 = 10

2.31   a. 5 fl. oz.
           b. 1 pint
           c. 5 cups
           d. 2 quarts
           e. 1 gallon
           f. 5 half gallons

2.32   a. 3 gallons
           b. 6 quarts
           c. 7 pints
           d. 3 quarts
           e. 28 fl. oz.
           f. 3 cups

SELF TEST 2

2.01 d

3 miles = 15,840 feet (not 15,480)

2.02 c

A football field is marked in yards.

2.03 a

A quarter is about an inch wide.

2.04 c

4 × 5,280 = 21,120

2.05 c

4 yards = 12 feet; 12 + 11 = 23

2.06 d

4 tons = 8,000 lb.

2.07 a

A cell phone would weigh less than a pound.

2.08 b

A laptop would weigh more than a pound, but less than 30 for it to be used on a person's lap.

2.09 a

48 ÷ 16 = 3

2.010 b

36 oz. ÷ 16 = 2 lb., 4 oz.
2 lb., 4 oz. + 4 lb. = 6 lb., 4 oz.

2.011 c

2 quarts = 8 cups = 64 fl. oz. = 4 pints

2.012 c

A pond would hold more than a gallon, or it would be a puddle.

2.013 a

A teacup holds a cup or less.

2.014 a

20 ÷ 2 = 10

2.015 c

4 cups = 2 pints
2 pints + 6 pints = 8 pints = 1 gallon

SECTION 3

3.1   a. 1
        b. 2

3.2   a. 4:15
        b. 5:00
        c. 6:45
        d. 8:20
        e. 9:55
        f. 2:10

3.3   a.

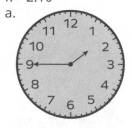   b.

      c.

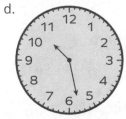

      e. d.

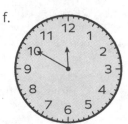

3.4   c

Most television shows are 30 minutes or one hour long.

3.5   c

Even the fastest jet would take over an hour, and an airline flight would be several hours.

3.6   c

80 + 40 = 120, 120 ÷ 60 = 2

3.7   b

4 hours, 10 minutes = 4 × 60 + 10 = 250.
2 hours, 20 minutes = 2 × 60 + 20 = 140 minutes.
250 – 140 = 110.
110 minutes = 1 hour, 50 minutes.

3.8   c

A typical school day is 5 to 6 hours long, although it might feel like a century.

3.9   c

1 hour = 60 minutes, 5 × 60 = 300

3.10   c

420 ÷ 60 = 7

3.11   d

480 ÷ 60 = 8

3.12   a. one half hour
         b. 40 minutes
         c. 1 hour, 20 minutes
         d. 85 minutes
         e. 3 hours, 10 minutes
         f. 200 minutes

3.13   a. 6 hours, 40 minutes
         b. 380 minutes
         c. 5 hours, 40 minutes
         d. 320 minutes
         e. 4 hours, 50 minutes
         f. 280 minutes

3.14   a. 3
         b. 1
         c. 2

3.15   a

6 – 2 = 4
55 – 45 = 10

3.16   b

8:40 to 11:40 = 3 hours
11:40 to 12:00 = 20 minutes

3.17   c

2:30 to 5:30 = 3 hours
5:30 to 6:15 = 45 minutes

3.18   c

8:30 to 12:30 = 4 hours
12:30 to 2:30 = 2 hours
2:30 to 3:20 = 50 minutes

3.19   d

10:15 + 4 hours = 14:15, or 2:15;
2:15 + 10 minutes = 2:25

3.20   b

9:15 to 12:15 = 3 hours
12:15 to 12:35 = 20 minutes
This is the longest elapsed time
by 5 minutes.

3.21   d

11:45 + 3 = 2:45
2:45 + :15 = 3:00

3.22   c

10:30 to 1:30 = 3 hours
3 hours – 15 minutes =
2 hours, 45 minutes

3.23   a.   3 hours, 0 minutes
       b.   3 hours, 45 minutes
       c.   3 hours, 15 minutes
       d.   6 hours, 30 minutes
       e.   4 hours, 15 minutes
       f.   4 hours, 45 minutes
       g.   3 hours, 45 minutes

3.24   a.   1
       b.   3
       c.   2

3.25   c

35°C = 95°F

3.26   b

5°C = 41°F

3.27   c

38.3°C = 101°F

3.28   a, c

35°C = 95°F

3.29   b, d

50°C = 122°F, so it would be very hot and
over 100°F.

3.30   a.   50°F, 10°C
       b.   70°F, 21°C
       c.   40°F, 5°C
       d.   185°F, 85°C

3.31   a.   b.   c.   d.

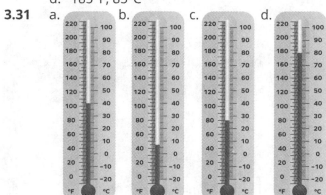

3.32   c

(1.8)(10) + 32 = 18 + 32 = 50

3.33   d

(1.8)(45) + 32 = 81 + 32 = 113

3.34   a

(0.55)(132 – 32) = (0.55)(100) = 55

3.35   a.   4
       b.   6
       c.   8
       d.   7
       e.   2
       f.   10
       g.   1
       h.   3
       i.   9
       j.   5

SELF TEST 3

3.01 d

> The drive would be more than 1 hour
> (unless the car drove 100 mph);
> 2 hours at 50 mph

3.02 c

> 1 hour = 60 minutes
> 8 × 60 = 480

3.03 d

> 90 + 50 = 140
> 140 ÷ 60 = 2 R20

3.04 a

> 1 hour = 60 minutes
> 3 × 60 = 180
> 180 + 50 = 230

3.05 c

> 3 hours, 50 minutes = 3 × 60 + 50
> = 230 minutes
> 5 hours, 20 minutes = 5 × 60 + 20
> = 320 minutes
> 320 – 230 = 90
> 90 minutes = 1 hour, 30 minutes

3.06 d

> 1:35 to 5:35 = 4 hours
> 5:35 to 6:00 = 25 minutes

3.07 b

> 7:30 + 3 hours = 10:30
> 10:30 + 50 minutes = 11:20

3.08 d

> 11:50 to 3:50 = 4 hours
> 3:50 to 4:05 = 15 minutes

3.09 b

> 10:15 to 3:15 = 5 hours
> 3:15 to 3:25 = 10 minutes
> This is the longest elapsed time
> by 5 minutes.

3.010 c

> 12:50 + 5 = 5:50
> 5:50 + :20 = 5:70 = 6:10

3.011 a

> It would be cool in autumn, but not cold.

3.012 b

> (1.8)(122) + 32 = 219.6 + 32 = 251.6

3.013 a

> (0.55)(124 – 32) = (0.55)(92) = 50.6

3.014 b

> The mercury level is at 90°F.

3.015 b, c

> 108°C = 226.4°F

SECTION 4

4.1 a. 3
    b. 7
    c. 16
    d. 18
    e. 10
    f. 19
    g. 20
    h. 4
    i. 15
    j. 17
    k. 6
    l. 8
    m. 13
    n. 12
    o. 11
    p. 5
    q. 9
    r. 14
    s. 1
    t. 2

4.2 c

"deca-" means "ten"

4.3 c

5 meters is about 14 feet.

4.4 a

$657 \div 1000 = 0.657$

4.5 d

$5.6 \times 1,000 = 5,600$

4.6 b, d

A truck would be very heavy, more than grams or pounds.

4.7 a, c

A glass is about 16 fluid ounces, close to 500 milliliters.

4.8 a

6 yards = 18 feet; 18 + 7 = 25 feet

4.9 c

(4 lb. + 12 oz.) + 4 oz. = 5 lb.

4.10 c

2 quarts = 8 cups = 4 pints = 64 fl. oz.

4.11 d

$75 + 55 = 130; 130 \div 60 = 2$ R10

4.12 b

10:50 to 3:50 = 5 hours, minus 5 minutes = 4 hours and 55 minutes

4.13 d

$(0.55)(232 - 32) = (0.55)(200) = 110$

LIFEPAC TEST

1. c

   There is one zero in 10, so the decimal moves one place to the left.

2. c

   "centi-" means "$\frac{1}{100}$"

3. c

   A bus would be several meters long.

4. d

   6.3 × 1,000 = 6,300. The decimal moves three places to the right.

5. a

   A flea is very small and would use the smallest units.

6. d

   789 ÷ 1,000 = 0.789. The decimal moves three places to the left.

7. c

   987 ÷ 1,000 = 0.987. The decimal moves three places to the left.

8. c

   Milliliters and fluid ounces are too small. A bathtub would hold several liters of water.

9. c

   4 × 5,280 = 21,120

10. a

    9 yards, 1 foot = 28 feet.
    28 feet – 8 feet = 20 feet.
    20 ÷ 3 = 6 R2; 6 yards, 2 feet.

11. d

    5 lb. = 80 oz. (5 × 16 = 80)
    80 + 10 = 90

12. c

    4 tons = 8,000 lb.
    8,000 – 350 = 7,650

13. c

    12 cups = 6 pints = 3 quarts = 48 fl. oz.

14. c

    4 quarts = 1 gallon, so 2 quarts = $\frac{1}{2}$ gallon.

    Each of the other measures are equal to 1 gallon.

15. b

    90 + 85 = 175
    175 ÷ 60 = 2 R55

16. d

    5 × 60 = 300

17. c

    8:50 + 4 = 12:50
    12:50 + :20 = 1:10

18. b

    4:25 to 7:25 = 3 hours
    7:25 to 7:40 = 15 minutes

19. c

    37°C = 98.6°F

20. d

    (1.8)(25) + 32 = 45 + 32 = 77

ALTERNATE LIFEPAC TEST

1.   d

> There are three zeros in 1,000, so the decimal moves three places to the right.

2.   c

> "kilo-" means "1,000"

3.   b

> All the units are longer than a pencil, except centimeters.

4.   d

> 35 × 1,000 = 35,000. The decimal moves three places to the right.

5.   c

> A nickel weighs 5 grams. (1 oz. ≈ 28 g)

6.   c

> 5.4 × 1,000 = 5,400. The decimal moves three places to the right.

7.   d

> 47 ÷ 1,000 = 0.047. The decimal moves three places to the left.

8.   a

> An apple is smaller than the volume of one liter, so milliliters would be used. Ounces measure weight (fl. oz. are for capacity).

9.   d

> 36 ÷ 3 = 12

10.   c

> 14 inches = 1 foot, 2 inches
> 5 feet – 1 foot = 4 feet
> 2 inches – 2 inches = 0 inches.

11.   c

> 3 tons = 6,000 lb.
> 6,000 + 560 = 6,560

12.   a

> 4 lb. = 64 oz.
> 64 – 12 = 52 oz.
> 52 ÷ 16 = 3 R4

13.   a

> 1 gallon = 16 cups = 128 fl. oz. = 4 quarts

14.   b

> 1 pint = 16 fl. oz.
> 6 pints = 96 fl. oz.

15.   c

> 75 + 85 = 160
> 160 ÷ 60 = 2 R40

16.   c

> 480 ÷ 60 = 8

17.   a

> 9:45 + 4 = 1:45
> 1:45 + :45 = 2:30

18.   c

> 2:05 to 6:05 = 4 hours
> 6:05 to 6:55 = 50 minutes

19.   c

> 100°C = 212°F

20.   b

> (1.8)(45) + 32 = 81 + 32 = 113

MATH 505

ALTERNATE LIFEPAC TEST

NAME _____

DATE _____

SCORE _____

Each numbered question = 5 points

Circle the correct letter and answer.

1. Solve the following: 4.76 × 1,000 = _____
   a. 0.0476   b. 047.6   c. 476   d. 4,760

2. Which prefix means "one thousand"?
   a. deca-   b. hecto-   c. kilo-   d. centi-

3. Which unit would you use to measure the length of a pencil?
   a. feet   b. cm   c. m   d. km

4. Convert 35 kilometers to meters.
   a. 0.035 m   b. 350 m   c. 3,500 m   d. 35,000 m

5. Which unit would you use to measure the weight of a nickel?
   a. ounces   b. mg   c. g   d. kg

6. Convert 5.4 kilograms to grams.
   a. 54 g   b. 540 g   c. 5,400 g   d. 0.0054 g

7. Which measurement is equivalent to 47 mL?
   a. 47,000 L   b. 4.7 L   c. 0.47 L   d. 0.047 L

8. Which unit would you use to measure the amount of water in an apple?
   a. mL   b. gallons   c. L   d. oz.

9. Convert 36 feet to yards.
   a. 3 yards   b. 6 yards   c. 9 yards   d. 12 yards

10. Subtract 14 inches from 5 feet, 2 inches.
    a. 6 feet   b. 6 feet ,4 inches   c. 4 feet   d. 4 feet, 2 inches

11. Convert 3 tons, 560 lb. to pounds.
    a. 3,560 lb.   b. 5,440 lb.   c. 6,560 lb.   d. 6,650 lb.

12. Subtract 12 ounces from 4 lb.
   a. 3 lb., 4 oz.
   b. 3 lb., 12 oz.
   c. 4 lb., 4 oz.
   d. 4 lb., 12 oz.

13. Which measurement is *not* equivalent to the others?
   a. 8 quarts
   b. 128 fl. oz.
   c. 1 gallon
   d. 16 cups

14. Which measurement is equivalent to 6 pints?
   a. 3 cups
   b. 96 fl. oz.
   c. 12 quarts
   d. 0.5 gallons

15. What is the sum of 75 minutes and 85 minutes?
   a. 10 minutes
   b. 2 hours
   c. 2 hours, 40 minutes
   d. 2 hours, 20 minutes

16. Convert 480 minutes to hours.
   a. 6 hours
   b. 7 hours
   c. 8 hours
   d. 10 hours

17. If it is 9:45 p.m., what will the time be 4 hours and 45 minutes later?
   a. 2:30 a.m.
   b. 1:30 a.m.
   c. 1:15 p.m.
   d. 2:45 p.m.

18. What is the elapsed time between 2:05 and 6:55?
   a. 4 hours
   b. 4 hours, 40 minutes
   c. 4 hours, 50 minutes
   d. 5 hours

19. What is the boiling point of water?
   a. 100°F
   b. 200°C
   c. 212°F
   d. 70°C

20. Convert 45°C to Fahrenheit.
   a. 100°F
   b. 113°F
   c. 127°F
   d. 140°F

MATH 506

Unit 6: Factors and Fractions

ANSWER KEYS

SECTION 1

1.1		Div. by 2	Div. by 3	Div. by 2 & 3
	a.		21	
	b.	16		
	c.			18
	d.	2		
	e.		15	
	f.		27	
	g.			6
	h.	8		
	i.	14		
	j.		9	
	k.			12
	l.			24

1.2 a. 2
      b. 1
      c. 4
      d. 3
1.3 a, b, c, e
1.4 a, c
1.5 b, d, f
1.6 b

The factors of 9 are 1, 3, and 9, so it is composite.

1.7 c

By definition, 1 is neither prime nor composite.

1.8 a

The only factors of 41 are 1 and 41, so it is prime.

1.9 b

The factors of 28 are 1, 2, 4, 7, 14, and 28, so it is composite.

1.10 a

The only factors of 17 are 1 and 17, so it is prime.

1.11 d
1.12 a, c, d, g
1.13 1, 2, 4, 7, 8, 14, 28, 56; Composite
1.14 1, 3, 5, 15; Composite
1.15 1, 19; Prime

1.16		Prime	Composite
	a.		9
	b.	7	
	c.		18
	d.	11	
	e.		10
	f.		4
	g.		15
	h.	13	
	i.	2	
	j.	19	

1.17 a. 2
       b. 1
1.18 a
1.19 b
1.20 d

$3 \times 3 \times 3 = 9 \times 3 = 27$

1.21 c

$2 \times 3 \times 7 = 6 \times 7 = 42$

1.22 $35 = 5 \times 7$
1.23 $63 = 3 \times 3 \times 7$
1.24 $72 = 2 \times 2 \times 2 \times 3 \times 3$
1.25 $48 = 2 \times 2 \times 2 \times 2 \times 3$
1.26 $56 = 2 \times 2 \times 2 \times 7$
1.27 a. 2
       b. 1
       c. 4
       d. 3
1.28 greatest common factor
1.29 b
1.30 d
1.31 b
1.32 b
1.33 a
1.34 d

1.35 7

28: 1, 2, 4, **7**, 15, 28
35: 1, 5, **7**, 35

1.36 1

16: 1, 2, 4, 8, 16
9: 1, 3, 9

1.37 12

48: 1, 2, 3, 4, 6, 8, **12**, 16, 24, 48
36: 1, 2, 3, 4, 6, 9, **12**, 18, 36

1.38 15

15: 1, 3, 5, **15**
45: 1, 3, 5, 9, **15**, 45

1.39 7

7: 1, **7**
21: 1, 3, **7**, 21

1.40 2

8: 1, **2**, 4, 8
6: 1, **2**, 3, 6
10: 1, **2**, 5, 10

1.41 1

14: 1, 2, 7, 14
20: 1, 2, 4, 5, 10, 20
25: 1, 5, 25

SELF TEST 1

1.01 false

1 is neither prime nor composite.

1.02 true

The sum of the digits is 15, which is divisible by 3. And, the number is even, so it's divisible by 2.

1.03 composite
1.04 prime
1.05 d

21: 1, 3, 7, 21

1.06 b

6: 1, **2**, 3, 6
14: 1, **2**, 7, 14

1.07 c

12: 1, 2, 3, **4**, 6, 12
4: 1, 2, **4**
28: 1, 2, **4**, 7, 14, 28

1.08 a

$2 \times 5 \times 5 = 10 \times 5 = 50$

1.09 d
1.010 b
1.011 a, b, c, d, e, g
1.012 3

12: 1, 2, **3**, 4, 6, 12
27: 1, **3**, 9, 27

1.013 1

18: 1, 2, 3, 6, 9, 18
11: 1, 11

1.014 1, 2, 3, 4, 6, 12
1.015 1, 3, 9, 27

SECTION 2

2.1   a. 2
         b. 1
         c. 3
         d. 4
2.2   d
2.3   a
2.4   b
2.5   b
2.6   d
2.7   a
2.8   c
2.9   b
2.10 Answers will vary but should include one of the following:
         Model: Of ten total items, four should be shaded or have the required element.
         Number line: The space between 0 and 1 should be divided into ten equal parts. A point should be drawn on the fourth tick mark.
2.11 a. 2
         b. 3
         c. 1
2.12 b
2.13 a

   Proper fractions are less than 1 in value.

2.14 c

   When the numerator and denominator are the same number, the fraction has a value of 1.

2.15 b

   Improper fractions are greater than or equal to 1 in value.

2.16 b

   $10 \div 7 = 1$ R3

2.17 a

   $20 \div 6 = 3$ R2

2.18 d

   $5 \div 2 = 2$ R1

2.19 c

   Numerator: $5 \times 3 + 2 = 17$;
   the denominator stays the same.

2.20 b

   Numerator: $2 \times 5 + 2 = 12$;
   the denominator stays the same.

2.21 d

   Numerator: $4 \times 7 + 6 = 34$;
   the denominator stays the same.

2.22 a. 4
         b. 2
         c. 1
         d. 3
2.23 simplest form
2.24 a. 8
         b. 7
         c. 6
         d. 5
         e. 3
         f. 4
         g. 2
         h. 12
         i. 1
2.25 a. 4
         b. 2
         c. 1
         d. 3
2.26 c

   9 and 12 have a common factor of 3. So, $\frac{9}{12}$ is not in simplest form.

2.27 a

   9 and 16 have no common factors, other than 1. So, $\frac{9}{16}$ is in simplest form.

2.28 d

   $\frac{32 \div 4}{36 \div 4} = \frac{8}{9}$

2.29 b

$$\frac{22 \div 11}{55 \div 11} = \frac{2}{5}$$

2.30 a. $\frac{3}{4}$

$$\frac{18 \div 6}{24 \div 6} = \frac{3}{4}$$

b. $\frac{1}{5}$

$$\frac{10 \div 10}{50 \div 10} = \frac{1}{5}$$

c. $\frac{2}{3}$

$$\frac{24 \div 12}{36 \div 12} = \frac{2}{3}$$

d. $\frac{7}{15}$

$$\frac{14 \div 2}{30 \div 2} = \frac{7}{15}$$

e. $\frac{9}{10}$

$$\frac{63 \div 7}{70 \div 7} = \frac{9}{10}$$

f. $\frac{5}{7}$

$$\frac{40 \div 8}{56 \div 8} = \frac{5}{7}$$

2.31 equivalent fractions

2.32 Answers will vary. In simplest form, $\frac{5}{20}$ is $\frac{1}{4}$.
So, students should write two fractions that
are equivalent to $\frac{1}{4}$. Some examples are $\frac{1}{4}$,
$\frac{2}{8}$, $\frac{10}{40}$, $\frac{15}{60}$, and $\frac{20}{80}$.

2.33 15

$$\frac{3 \times 5}{10 \times 5} = \frac{15}{50}$$

2.34 63

$$\frac{2 \times 7}{9 \times 7} = \frac{14}{63}$$

2.35 24

$$\frac{12 \times 2}{18 \times 2} = \frac{24}{36}$$

2.36 19

$$\frac{30 \div 2}{38 \div 2} = \frac{15}{19}$$

2.37 20

$$\frac{60 \div 3}{66 \div 3} = \frac{20}{22}$$

2.38 6

$$\frac{24 \div 8}{48 \div 8} = \frac{3}{6}$$

2.39 true

Both fractions reduce to $\frac{2}{3}$.

2.40 false

Both fractions are already written in
simplest form, but they don't look the
same.

2.41 true

Both fractions reduce to $\frac{1}{6}$.

2.42 b

$$\frac{3 \times 3}{8 \times 3} = \frac{9}{24}$$

2.43 c

$\frac{4}{7}$ is already in simplest form and is not
the same as $\frac{1}{2}$.

2.44	a
2.45	d
2.46	a
2.47	d
2.48	d
2.49	d
2.50	a
2.51	c

SELF TEST 2

2.01 false

$$\frac{16 \div 4}{20 \div 4} = \frac{4}{5}$$

2.02 false

$8\frac{1}{2}$ is a mixed number.

2.03 a

2.04 b

2.05 d

2.06 a

Proper fractions are less than 1 in value.

2.07 b

$19 \div 5 = 3 \text{ R}4$

2.08 d

Numerator: $7 \times 8 + 1 = 57$;
the denominator stays the same.

2.09 c

$$\frac{10 \times 4}{12 \times 4} = \frac{40}{48}$$

2.010 b, c, d

Fractions are in simplest form when the numerator and denominator have no common factors.

2.011 a, b, c, e

$\frac{4}{12}, \frac{9}{27}, \frac{5}{15},$ and $\frac{8}{24}$ are all written as $\frac{1}{3}$.

2.012 $\frac{7}{10}$

2.013 $\frac{7}{16}$

$$\frac{14 \div 2}{32 \div 2} = \frac{7}{16}$$

2.014 24

$$\frac{6 \times 4}{9 \times 4} = \frac{24}{36}$$

2.015 7

$$\frac{35 \div 7}{49 \div 7} = \frac{5}{7}$$

SECTION 3

3.1 a. 1
  b. 2
3.2 c, d, e, g
3.3 a, b, d, e, g
3.4 b, c, d, g
3.5 b

15: 15, 30, 45, **60**
20: 20, 40, **60**
The LCM of 15 and 20 is 60. So, the teacher should buy 60 sheets of stickers, which is 4 packages.

3.6 60

10: 10, 20, 30, 40, 50, **60**
12: 12, 24, 36, 48, **60**

3.7 6

2: 2, 4, **6**, 8, 10, 12
6: 6, 12

3.8 16

8: 8, **16**, 24, 32
16: 16, 32

3.9 15

3: 3, 6, 9, 12, **15**
5: 5, 10, **15**, 20

3.10 36

9: 9, 18, 27, **36**
12: 12, 24, **36**

3.11 42

6: 6, 12, 18, 24, 30, 36, **42**
14: 14, 28, **42**

3.12 a. 1
  b. 5
  c. 4
  d. 8
  e. 2
  f. 6
  g. 3
  h. 7

3.13 a. 3
      b. 2
      c. 1

3.14 a

3.15 b

The LCD is 42.

$$\frac{3 \times 7}{6 \times 7} = \frac{21}{42}$$

$$\frac{3 \times 6}{7 \times 6} = \frac{18}{42}$$

3.16 b

The whole number 7 is greater than the whole number 6. So, $7\frac{3}{8}$ is greater than $6\frac{6}{7}$.

3.17 a

The LCD is 24.

$$4\frac{5 \times 3}{8 \times 3} = 4\frac{15}{24}$$

$$4\frac{2 \times 8}{3 \times 8} = 4\frac{16}{24}$$

3.18 c

The LCD is 10.

$$\frac{1 \times 5}{2 \times 5} = \frac{5}{10}$$

3.19 b

The LCD is 24.

$$3\frac{7 \times 3}{8 \times 3} = 3\frac{21}{24}$$

$$3\frac{5 \times 4}{6 \times 4} = 3\frac{20}{24}$$

3.20 b

3.21 a

The LCD is 36.

$$\frac{5 \times 3}{12 \times 3} = \frac{15}{36}$$

$$\frac{4 \times 4}{9 \times 4} = \frac{16}{36}$$

3.22 c

The LCD is 16.

$$5\frac{5 \times 2}{8 \times 2} = 5\frac{10}{16}$$

3.23 a

The LCD is 15.

Rochelle: $8\frac{2 \times 5}{3 \times 5} = 8\frac{10}{15}$

Mario: $8\frac{7}{15}$

Ryan: $8\frac{3 \times 3}{5 \times 3} = 8\frac{9}{15}$

3.24 b

The LCD is 15.

Rochelle: $8\frac{2 \times 5}{3 \times 5} = 8\frac{10}{15}$

Mario: $8\frac{7}{15}$

Ryan: $8\frac{3 \times 3}{5 \times 3} = 8\frac{9}{15}$

3.25 $6\frac{1}{2}$ $6\frac{5}{8}$ $6\frac{3}{4}$

3.26 $\frac{2}{6}$ $\frac{2}{3}$ $\frac{11}{12}$

3.27 a, c

3.28 b

3.29 c

3.30 d

3.31 a

3.32 a

3.33 d

3.34 c

3.35 b

3.36 a. 1
      b. 3
      c. 4
      d. 2

3.37 a. 2
      b. 5
      c. 4
      d. 1
      e. 3

3.38 fraction: $\frac{1}{5}$ decimal: 0.2

3.39 rounding

3.40 b

> The LCD is 10.
>
> $\dfrac{1 \times 5}{2 \times 5} = \dfrac{5}{10}$

3.41 c

> The LCD is 12.
>
> $\dfrac{1 \times 6}{2 \times 6} = \dfrac{6}{12}$

3.42 b

> The LCD is 30.
>
> $\dfrac{1 \times 15}{2 \times 15} = \dfrac{15}{30}$
>
> $\dfrac{7 \times 2}{15 \times 2} = \dfrac{14}{30}$

3.43 a

> The LCD is 26.
>
> $\dfrac{1 \times 13}{2 \times 13} = \dfrac{13}{26}$
>
> $\dfrac{8 \times 2}{13 \times 2} = \dfrac{16}{26}$

3.44 b

3.45 c

3.46 a

3.47 b

3.48 a. 1

> $\dfrac{5}{8}$ is greater than $\dfrac{1}{2}$ (or $\dfrac{4}{8}$), so $\dfrac{5}{8}$ rounds up to 1.

b. 0

> $\dfrac{2}{9}$ (or $\dfrac{4}{18}$) is less than $\dfrac{1}{2}$ (or $\dfrac{9}{18}$), so $\dfrac{2}{9}$ rounds down to 0.

c. 7

> $\dfrac{3}{8}$ is less than $\dfrac{1}{2}$ (or $\dfrac{4}{8}$), so $7\dfrac{3}{8}$ rounds down to 7.

d. 5

> $\dfrac{2}{7}$ (or $\dfrac{4}{14}$) is less than $\dfrac{1}{2}$ (or $\dfrac{7}{14}$), so $5\dfrac{2}{7}$ rounds down to 5.

e. 4

> $\dfrac{2}{3}$ (or $\dfrac{4}{6}$) is greater than $\dfrac{1}{2}$ (or $\dfrac{3}{6}$), so $3\dfrac{2}{3}$ rounds up to 4.

SELF TEST 3

3.01   false
3.02   true
3.03   false

$$\frac{3 \times 25}{4 \times 25} = \frac{75}{100} = 0.75$$

3.04   b, c, e, f
3.05   d

6: 6, 12, **18**,
9: 9, **18**

3.06   b
3.07   c

A fraction is equivalent to $\frac{1}{2}$ if the numerator is exactly half of the denominator.

3.08   a
3.09   a

The LCD is 35.

$$7\frac{2 \times 7}{5 \times 7} = 7\frac{14}{35}$$

$$7\frac{3 \times 5}{7 \times 5} = 7\frac{15}{35}$$

3.010   b

$$\frac{4 \times 2}{5 \times 2} = \frac{8}{10} = 0.8$$

3.011   b

There are 5 shaded circles out of 10 total circles.

$$\frac{5 \div 5}{10 \div 5} = \frac{1}{2}$$

3.012   d

$$\frac{5}{10} = 0.5$$

3.013   14

2: 2, 4, 6, 8, 10, 12, **14**,
7: 7, **14**

3.014   7

$$7\frac{3 \times 2}{7 \times 2} = 7\frac{6}{14}$$

$\frac{6}{14}$ is less than $\frac{1}{2}$, or $\frac{7}{14}$. So, the mixed number rounds down to 7.

3.015   1

$\frac{7}{8}$ is greater than $\frac{1}{2}$, or $\frac{4}{8}$. So, the fraction rounds up to 1.

SECTION 4

4.1   a. 2
         b. 6
         c. 4
         d. 5
         e. 8
         f. 3
         g. 7
         h. 9
         i. 1

4.2   a. 9
         b. 6
         c. 7
         d. 5
         e. 2
         f. 4
         g. 10
         h. 11
         i. 1
         j. 8
         k. 3

4.3   true

4.4   false

15 has four factors (1, 3, 5, 15), so it is composite.

4.5   true

The fractions look the same in simplest form, so they are equivalent fractions.

$$\frac{4 \div 2}{10 \div 2} = \frac{2}{5}$$

$$\frac{6 \div 3}{15 \div 3} = \frac{2}{5}$$

4.6   c

25: 1, 5, **25**
50: 1, 2, 5, 10, **25**, 50

4.7   d

3: 3, 6, 9, 12, 15, 18, **21**
7: 7, 14, **21**, 28

4.8   b

There are 3 boys and 9 total kids.

4.9   a

$$\frac{3 \div 3}{9 \div 3} = \frac{1}{3}$$

4.10   b

$\frac{11}{2}$ is an improper fraction, so it has a value greater than 1.

4.11   a

The LCM of 4 and 6 is 12.

$$9\frac{3 \times 3}{4 \times 3} = 9\frac{9}{12}$$

$$9\frac{5 \times 2}{6 \times 2} = 9\frac{10}{12}$$

4.12   b

The LCM of 2 and 7 is 14.

$$\frac{1 \times 7}{2 \times 7} = \frac{7}{14}$$

$$\frac{2 \times 2}{7 \times 2} = \frac{4}{14}$$

4.13   c

$$0.8 = \frac{8}{10}$$

$$\frac{8 \div 2}{10 \div 2} = \frac{4}{5}$$

LIFEPAC TEST

1. true

> The factors of 24 are 1, 2, 3, 4, 6, 8, 12, and 24.

2. false

> 4 and 18 have a common factor of 2.
> $$\frac{4 \div 2}{18 \div 2} = \frac{2}{9}$$

3. b
4. a
5. a
6. c

> $\frac{5}{9}$ (or $\frac{10}{18}$) is greater than $\frac{1}{2}$ (or $\frac{9}{18}$), so the mixed number rounds up to 9.

7. b

> The LCD is 40.
> $$7\frac{2 \times 8}{5 \times 8} = 7\frac{16}{40}$$
> $$7\frac{3 \times 5}{8 \times 5} = 7\frac{15}{40}$$

8. c
9. c

> The GCF of 6 and 16 is 2, not 3.

10. c

> Justin has four total pets, and three are goldfish.

11. d

> $$\frac{3 \times 25}{4 \times 25} = \frac{75}{100} = 0.75$$

12. b

> $$0.02 = \frac{2 \div 2}{100 \div 2} = \frac{1}{50}$$

13. d

> Numerator: $3 \times 11 + 4 = 33 + 4 = 37$.
> The denominator stays the same.

14. c

> 4 goes into 26 six times, with a remainder of 2.
> $$\frac{26}{4} = 6\frac{2 \div 2}{4 \div 2} = 6\frac{1}{2}$$

15. b

> $\frac{8}{22}$, $\frac{12}{33}$, and $\frac{16}{44}$ all reduce to $\frac{4}{11}$.

16. a

> $$\frac{5 \times 3}{6 \times 3} = \frac{15}{18}$$

17. $\frac{5}{12}$ $\frac{2}{3}$ $\frac{5}{6}$

> The LCD is 12.
> $$\frac{2 \times 4}{3 \times 4} = \frac{8}{12}$$
> $$\frac{5 \times 2}{6 \times 2} = \frac{10}{12}$$

18. 9

> List the factors of each number.
> **9:** 1, 3, **9**
> **18:** 1, 2, 3, 6, **9**, 18

19. 18

> List the multiples of each number.
> **9:** 9, **18**, 27
> **18:** **18**, 36, 54

20. Answers will vary. Possible answers include 9, 18, 27, 36, 45, 54, and 63.

ALTERNATE LIFEPAC TEST

1. false

> The factors of 9 are 1, 3, and 9.

2. true
3. a
4. b
5. a
6. b

> $\frac{6}{13}$ (or $\frac{12}{26}$) is less than $\frac{1}{2}$ (or $\frac{13}{26}$), so the mixed number rounds down to 5.

7. c

> The LCD is 30.
> $4\frac{2 \times 5}{6 \times 5} = 4\frac{10}{30}$
>
> $4\frac{5 \times 2}{15 \times 2} = 4\frac{10}{30}$

8. d
9. d
10. b

> There are five total people and two have blue eyes.

11. a

> $\frac{2 \times 2}{5 \times 2} = \frac{4}{10} = 0.4$

12. c

> $0.14 = \frac{14 \div 2}{100 \div 2} = \frac{7}{50}$

13. a

> Numerator: $8 \times 9 + 5 = 72 + 5 = 77$.
> The denominator stays the same.

14. d

> 8 goes into 46 five times, with a remainder of 6.
> $\frac{46}{8} = 5\frac{6 \div 2}{8 \div 2} = 5\frac{3}{4}$

15. a

> $\frac{6}{21}$, $\frac{4}{14}$, and $\frac{12}{42}$ all reduce to $\frac{2}{7}$.

16. b

> $\frac{7 \times 3}{8 \times 3} = \frac{21}{24}$

17. $\frac{1}{2}$ $\frac{7}{12}$ $\frac{3}{4}$

> The LCD is 12.
> $\frac{1 \times 6}{2 \times 6} = \frac{6}{12}$
>
> $\frac{3 \times 3}{4 \times 3} = \frac{9}{12}$

18. 8

> List the factors of each number.
> **8:** 1, 2, 4, **8**
> **16:** 1, 2, 4, **8**, 16

19. 16

> List the multiples of each number.
> **8:** 8, **16**, 24, 32
> **16:** **16**, 32, 48

20. Answers will vary. Possible answers include 8, 16, 24, 32, 40, and 48.

MATH 506

ALTERNATE LIFEPAC TEST

NAME _____

DATE _____

SCORE _____

Each numbered question = 5 points

Answer *true* or *false*.

1. _____ The number 9 has four factors.

2. _____ The fraction $\frac{4}{15}$ is in simplest form.

Circle the correct letter and answer.

3. $\frac{5}{5}$ is _____ fraction.
   a. an improper   b. a proper

4. 6 is a _____ of 18.
   a. multiple   b. factor

5. 6 is a _____ number.
   a. composite   b. prime

6. Round $5\frac{6}{13}$ to the nearest whole number.
   a. 4   b. 5   c. 6   d. 7

7. Compare using <, >, or =. $4\frac{2}{6}$ _____ $4\frac{5}{15}$
   a. <   b. >   c. =

8. What is the prime factorization of 52?
   a. 2 × 23   b. 2 × 26   c. 4 × 13   d. 2 × 2 × 13

9. Which of the following statements are true?
   I. The GCF of 4 and 18 is 2.
   II. The LCM of 4 and 18 is 36.
   III. 4 and 18 are both composite numbers.
   a. I and II   b. I and III   c. II and III   d. They are all true.

10. In Charlie's family, two people have blue eyes, and three people have brown eyes. Write a fraction to represent the part of the family that has blue eyes.

    a. $\frac{2}{3}$ b. $\frac{2}{5}$ c. $\frac{3}{5}$ d. $\frac{3}{2}$

11. In Charlie's family, two people have blue eyes, and three people have brown eyes. Write a decimal number to represent the part of the family that has blue eyes.

    a. 0.4   b. 0.6   c. 0.04   d. 0.06

12. Rewrite 0.14 as a fraction in simplest form.

    a. $\frac{10}{14}$ b. $\frac{5}{7}$ c. $\frac{7}{50}$ d. $\frac{14}{100}$

13. Rewrite $8\frac{5}{9}$ as an improper fraction.

    a. $\frac{77}{9}$ b. $\frac{49}{9}$ c. $\frac{49}{5}$ d. $\frac{22}{9}$

14. Rewrite $\frac{46}{8}$ as a mixed number in simplest form.

    a. $5\frac{6}{8}$ b. $6\frac{2}{8}$ c. $6\frac{1}{4}$ d. $5\frac{3}{4}$

15. Which of the following fractions is *not* equivalent to $\frac{6}{21}$?

    a. $\frac{3}{7}$ b. $\frac{2}{7}$ c. $\frac{4}{14}$ d. $\frac{12}{42}$

16. Find n. $\frac{7}{8} = \frac{21}{n}$

    a. $n = 22$ b. $n = 24$ c. $n = 3$ d. $n = 16$

Place these fractions in order from smallest to largest.

17. $\frac{1}{2}$ $\frac{7}{12}$ $\frac{3}{4}$

    _____   _____   _____

Complete these activities.

18. What is the GCF of 8 and 16?   _____

19. What is the LCM of 8 and 16?   _____

20. List three multiples of 8.   _____

MATH 507

Unit 7: Fraction Operations

ANSWER KEYS

SECTION 1

1.1   c
1.2   b
1.3   a

$$\frac{4}{10} + \frac{2}{10} = \frac{6 \div 2}{10 \div 2} = \frac{3}{5}$$

1.4   d

$$\frac{2}{5} + \frac{2}{5} + \frac{3}{5} = \frac{7}{5} = 1\frac{2}{5}$$

1.5   c

$$\frac{5}{8} + \frac{7}{8} = \frac{12}{8} = 1\frac{4 \div 4}{8 \div 4} = 1\frac{1}{2}$$

1.6   c

$$\frac{2}{4} + \frac{3}{4} = \frac{5}{4} = 1\frac{1}{4}$$

1.7   b
1.8   d

$$\frac{5}{6} - \frac{3}{6} = \frac{2 \div 2}{6 \div 2} = \frac{1}{3}$$

1.9   b

$$\frac{6}{9} - \frac{3}{9} = \frac{3 \div 3}{9 \div 3} = \frac{1}{3}$$

1.10 $\frac{6}{7}$

1.11 $\frac{1}{2}$

$$\frac{9}{10} - \frac{4}{10} = \frac{5 \div 5}{10 \div 5} = \frac{1}{2}$$

1.12   a. 5
          b. 4
          c. 2
          d. 1
          e. 3
          f. 6

1.13   a
1.14   b
1.15   a
1.16   d
1.17   b
1.18   a
1.19   a
1.20   c

$$2\frac{2}{9} + 1\frac{4}{9} = 3\frac{6}{9} = 3\frac{2}{3}$$

1.21   b

$$4\frac{6}{7} + 3\frac{5}{7} = 7\frac{11}{7} = 7 + 1\frac{4}{7} = 8\frac{4}{7}$$

1.22   d

$$5\frac{2}{6} = 4\frac{2}{6} + \frac{6}{6} = 4\frac{8}{6}$$

1.23   a

$$4\frac{1}{4} + 3\frac{3}{4} = 7\frac{4}{4} = 7 + 1 = 8$$

1.24   b
1.25   d

$$4\frac{5}{8} - 1\frac{1}{8} = 3\frac{4}{8} = 3\frac{1}{2}$$

1.26   b

$$1\frac{4}{4} - \frac{1}{4} = 1\frac{3}{4}$$

1.27   c

$$5\frac{2}{6} = 4\frac{8}{6}$$

$$4\frac{8}{6} - 2\frac{3}{6} = 2\frac{5}{6}$$

1.28   b

$$4\frac{1}{4} = 3\frac{5}{4}$$

$$3\frac{5}{4} - 3\frac{3}{4} = \frac{2}{4} = \frac{1}{2}$$

1.29   a

$$4\frac{1}{4} = 3\frac{1}{4} + \frac{4}{4} = 3\frac{5}{4}$$

1.30   a. 4
           b. 3
           c. 1
           d. 2

1.31   about

1.32   a

4 is very small compared to 27. So, the mixed number rounds down.

1.33   c

5 is very close to 6. So, the mixed number rounds up.

1.34   b

8 is a little more than half of 14. So, the fraction rounds to the nearest half.

1.35   c

Estimate: 10 + 6 = 16

1.36   b

Estimate: $6\frac{1}{2} + 8 = 14\frac{1}{2}$

1.37   c

9 is close to 10, so the mixed number rounds up.

1.38   b

Estimate: 20 + 37 = 57

1.39   d

$$45\frac{1}{2} - 37 = 8\frac{1}{2}$$

1.40   a

Estimate: 10 – 6 = 4

1.41   d

Estimate: $7\frac{1}{2} - 2 = 5\frac{1}{2}$

1.42   b
1.43   c
1.44   c
1.45   b

SELF TEST 1

1.01 false

$$\frac{1}{3} + \frac{1}{3} = \frac{2}{3}$$

1.02 true

$$\frac{3}{3} - \frac{2}{3} = \frac{1}{3}$$

1.03 c

$$\frac{3}{7} + \frac{4}{7} = \frac{7}{7} = 1$$

1.04 d

$$\frac{9}{12} + \frac{6}{12} = \frac{15}{12} = 1\frac{3}{12} = 1\frac{1}{4}$$

1.05 c

$$5\frac{2}{2} - 1\frac{1}{2} = 4\frac{1}{2}$$

1.06 b

$$4\frac{7}{8} - 2\frac{3}{8} = 2\frac{4}{8} = 2\frac{1}{2}$$

1.07 d

$$8 + 1\frac{1}{2} = 9\frac{1}{2}$$

1.08 b

$$7 - 2 = 5$$

1.09 a

$$6\frac{3}{8} - 5\frac{5}{8} = 5\frac{11}{8} - 5\frac{5}{8} = \frac{6}{8} = \frac{3}{4}$$

1.010 c

$$5\frac{1}{6} + 4\frac{5}{6} = 9\frac{6}{6} = 10$$

1.011 b

5 is about half of 8, so $\frac{5}{8}$ rounds to the nearest half.

1.012 c

5 is close in value to 6, so $\frac{5}{6}$ rounds up to the next whole number.

1.013 b

$$5\frac{1}{2} - 5 = \frac{1}{2}$$

1.014 $\frac{2}{5}$

$$\frac{9}{10} - \frac{5}{10} = \frac{4}{10} = \frac{2}{5}$$

1.015 $\frac{5}{8}$

$$\frac{1}{8} + \frac{4}{8} = \frac{5}{8}$$

SECTION 2

2.1   a. 4
        b. 2
        c. 1
        d. 3

2.2   a

> The LCD is 28.
> $\frac{7}{28} + \frac{20}{28} = \frac{27}{28}$

2.3   c

> She has finished $\frac{27}{28}$ of her homework.
>
> Since 27 is close to 28, she has just a little left to finish.

2.4   b

> **5:** 5, **10**, 15, 20
> **10: 10**, 20, 30, 40

2.5   d

> The LCD is 10.
> $\frac{4}{10} + \frac{1}{10} = \frac{5}{10} = \frac{1}{2}$

2.6   c

> **3:** 3, 6, 9, **12**
> **4:** 4, 8, **12**, 16

2.7   b

> The LCD is 12.
> $\frac{4}{12} + \frac{3}{12} = \frac{7}{12}$

2.8   c

> The LCD is 8.
> $\frac{4}{8} + \frac{7}{8} = \frac{11}{8} = 1\frac{3}{8}$

2.9   a

> The LCD is 18.
> $\frac{15}{18} + \frac{6}{18} = \frac{21}{18} = 1\frac{3}{18} = 1\frac{1}{6}$

2.10   a
2.11   a
2.12   d
2.13   b
2.14 $\frac{31}{40}$

> The LCD is 40.
> $\frac{15}{40} + \frac{16}{40} = \frac{31}{40}$

2.15 $\frac{3}{4}$

> The LCD is 12.
> $\frac{5}{12} + \frac{4}{12} = \frac{9}{12} = \frac{3}{4}$

2.16   a. 8
         b. 4
         c. 3
         d. 6

2.17   Fraction

2.18   a. 1
         b. 4
         c. 2
         d. 3

2.19   b

> **8: 8**, 16, 24, 32
> **4:** 4, **8**, 12, 16

2.20   a

> The LCD is 8.
> $\frac{7}{8} - \frac{6}{8} = \frac{1}{8}$

2.21   d

> **6:** 6, 12, 18, 24, **30**
> **5:** 5, 10, 15, 20, 25, **30**

2.22   c

> The LCD is 30.
> $\frac{25}{30} - \frac{12}{30} = \frac{13}{30}$

2.23 d

The LCD is 10.

$\frac{7}{10} - \frac{5}{10} = \frac{2}{10} = \frac{1}{5}$

2.24 c

The LCD is 12.

$\frac{11}{12} - \frac{9}{12} = \frac{2}{12} = \frac{1}{6}$

2.25 a

The LCD is 9.

$\frac{6}{9} - \frac{2}{9} = \frac{4}{9}$

2.26 b

$\frac{4}{9}$ of the pizza is left. 4 is about half of 9, so about half of the pizza is left.

2.27 $\frac{7}{24}$

The LCD is 24.

$\frac{16}{24} - \frac{9}{24} = \frac{7}{24}$

2.28 $\frac{1}{3}$

The LCD is 12.

$\frac{9}{12} - \frac{5}{12} = \frac{4}{12} = \frac{1}{3}$

2.29 c
2.30 a
2.31 a
2.32 b
2.33 b
2.34 c

6: 6, 12, 18, 24, 30, 36, **42**
7: 7, 14, 21, 28, 35, **42**

2.35 a

The LCD is 42.

$4\frac{7}{42} + 5\frac{24}{42} = 9\frac{31}{42}$

2.36 d

9: 9, 18, 27, **36**, 45
12: 12, 24, **36**, 48

2.37 b

The LCD is 36.

$3\frac{32}{36} + 1\frac{15}{36} = 4\frac{47}{36} = 4 + 1\frac{11}{36} = 5\frac{11}{36}$

2.38 b

The LCD is 12.

$6\frac{10}{12} + 6\frac{11}{12} = 12\frac{21}{12} = 12 + 1\frac{9}{12} = 13\frac{9}{12} = 13\frac{3}{4}$

2.39 d

The LCD is 10.

$1\frac{5}{10} + 2\frac{3}{10} = 3\frac{8}{10} = 3\frac{4}{5}$

2.40 c

The LCD is 12.

$4\frac{8}{12} + 3\frac{9}{12} = 7\frac{17}{12} = 7 + 1\frac{5}{12} = 8\frac{5}{12}$

2.41 b

The LCD is 8.

$2\frac{1}{8} + 1\frac{6}{8} = 3\frac{7}{8}$

2.42 $5\frac{5}{12}$

The LCD is 12.

$3\frac{3}{12} + 2\frac{2}{12} = 5\frac{5}{12}$

2.43 $6\frac{3}{16}$

The LCD is 16.

$4\frac{9}{16} + 1\frac{10}{16} = 5\frac{19}{16} = 5 + 1\frac{3}{16} = 6\frac{3}{16}$

2.44 a. Find the LCD of the fractions.
b. Rewrite each fraction using the LCD.
c. Add the mixed numbers using the rewritten fractions.
d. Write the sum in simplest form.

2.45 a
2.46 b

9: 9, 18, 27, 36
3: 3, 6, **9**, 12, 15

2.47   a

The LCD is 9.

$4\frac{7}{9} - 2\frac{6}{9} = 2\frac{1}{9}$

2.48   d

8: 8, 16, **24**, 32
12: 12, **24**, 36

2.49   a

Subtract 1 from the whole number part and add $\frac{24}{24}$ to the fraction part.

2.50   c

The LCD is 24.

$8\frac{10}{24} - 3\frac{15}{24} = 7\frac{34}{24} - 3\frac{15}{24} = 4\frac{19}{24}$

2.51   c

The LCD is 12.

$8\frac{5}{12} - 7\frac{3}{12} = 1\frac{2}{12} = 1\frac{1}{6}$

2.52   b

The LCD is 8.

$4\frac{7}{8} - 4\frac{2}{8} = \frac{5}{8}$

2.53   d

Estimate: $9\frac{1}{2} - 2 = 7\frac{1}{2}$

2.54   d
2.55   d
2.56   b
2.57   d
2.58 $7\frac{9}{14}$

The LCD is 14.

$9\frac{7}{14} - 1\frac{12}{14} = 8\frac{21}{14} - 1\frac{12}{14} = 7\frac{9}{14}$

2.59 $4\frac{3}{5}$

The LCD is 20.

$6\frac{15}{20} - 2\frac{3}{20} = 4\frac{12}{20} = 4\frac{3}{5}$

SELF TEST 2

2.01   false

10: 10, **20**, 30, 40
4: 4, 8, 12, 16, **20**

2.02   true

4: 4, 8, **12**, 16, 20
12: **12**, 24, 36, 48

2.03   a

The LCD is 6.

$\frac{3}{6} + \frac{4}{6} = \frac{7}{6} = 1\frac{1}{6}$

2.04   d

The LCD is 12.

$5\frac{9}{12} + 2\frac{11}{12} = 7\frac{20}{12} = 8\frac{8}{12} = 8\frac{2}{3}$

2.05   c

The LCD is 12.

$5\frac{9}{12} - 2\frac{11}{12} = 4\frac{21}{12} - 2\frac{11}{12} = 2\frac{10}{12} = 2\frac{5}{6}$

2.06   a

Borrow 1 from the whole number part and add $\frac{5}{5}$ to the fraction part.

2.07   d

The LCD is 20.

$\frac{14}{20} + \frac{5}{20} = \frac{19}{20}$

2.08   b

The LCD is 20.

$\frac{14}{20} - \frac{5}{20} = \frac{9}{20}$

2.09   c

The LCD is 18.

$\frac{11}{18} + \frac{4}{18} = \frac{15}{18} = \frac{5}{6}$

2.010 d

The LCD is 18.
$\frac{11}{18} - \frac{3}{18} = \frac{8}{18} = \frac{4}{9}$

2.011 b

$3\frac{1}{3} + 4\frac{1}{12} = 3\frac{4}{12} + 4\frac{1}{12} = 7\frac{5}{12}$

2.012 c

$4\frac{1}{12} - 3\frac{1}{3} = 4\frac{1}{12} - 3\frac{4}{12} = 3\frac{13}{12} - 3\frac{4}{12} = \frac{9}{12} = \frac{3}{4}$

2.013 $\frac{7}{15}$

The LCD is 15.
$\frac{13}{15} - \frac{6}{15} = \frac{7}{15}$

2.014 $6\frac{7}{30}$

The LCD is 30.
$2\frac{25}{30} + 3\frac{12}{30} = 5\frac{37}{30} = 6\frac{7}{30}$

2.015 $4\frac{3}{14}$

The LCD is 14.
$5\frac{7}{14} - 1\frac{4}{14} = 4\frac{3}{14}$

SECTION 3

3.1 c

3.2 a

Multiplying a whole number by a value less than 1 results in a smaller product.

3.3 b

Multiplying a whole number by a value greater than 1 results in a larger product.

3.4 c

Multiplying a whole number by 1 results in the same number.

3.5 a

$24 \div 3 = 8$
$2 \times 8 = 16$

3.6 b

$40 \div 10 = 4$
$7 \times 4 = 28$

3.7 a. 1
b. 2
c. 3

3.8 15

$18 \div 6 = 3$
$5 \times 3 = 15$

3.9 8

$32 \div 4 = 8$
$1 \times 8 = 8$

3.10 10

$35 \div 7 = 5$
$2 \times 5 = 10$

3.11 18

$48 \div 8 = 6$
$3 \times 6 = 18$

3.12 12

$15 \div 5 = 3$
$4 \times 3 = 12$

3.13 a. 2
b. 3
c. 6
d. 1
e. 5
f. 4
3.14 model, pencil, paper
3.15 b
3.16 c
3.17 d

$$\frac{1 \times 2}{8 \times 3} = \frac{2}{24} = \frac{1}{12}$$

3.18 a

$$\frac{4 \times 2}{9 \times 3} = \frac{8}{27}$$

3.19 c

$$\frac{5 \times 7}{7 \times 10} = \frac{35}{70} = \frac{1}{2}$$

3.20 a

$$\frac{3 \times 1}{4 \times 2} = \frac{3}{8}$$

3.21 b

$$\frac{2 \times 1}{3 \times 3} = \frac{2}{9}$$

3.22 a

$$\frac{5 \times 5}{8 \times 6} = \frac{25}{48}$$

3.23 a. $\frac{1}{3}$

$$\frac{5 \times 4}{12 \times 5} = \frac{20}{60} = \frac{1}{3}$$

b. $\frac{7}{44}$

$$\frac{7 \times 1}{11 \times 4} = \frac{7}{44}$$

c. $\frac{1}{18}$

$$\frac{1 \times 1}{3 \times 6} = \frac{1}{18}$$

3.24 a. 3
b. 6
c. 1
d. 2
e. 4
f. 5
3.25 multiplied, multiplied
3.26 a. 2
b. 1
c. 4
d. 3
3.27 a
3.28 c
3.29 b

$$1\frac{2}{3} \times \frac{4}{5} = \frac{5}{3} \times \frac{4}{5} = \frac{4}{3} = 1\frac{1}{3}$$

3.30 c
3.31 b
3.32 c
3.33 b
3.34 c

Because 6 is being multiplied by a value that is greater than 1, the product will be greater than 6.

3.35 d
3.36 b

$$\frac{11}{6} \times \frac{2}{1} = \frac{22}{6} = 3\frac{4}{6} = 3\frac{2}{3}$$

3.37 a. $\frac{22}{35}$

$$\frac{11}{7} \times \frac{2}{5} = \frac{22}{35}$$

b. $9\frac{1}{6}$

$$\frac{5}{2} \times \frac{11}{3} = \frac{55}{6} = 9\frac{1}{6}$$

c. $5\frac{1}{4}$

$$\frac{7}{1} \times \frac{3}{4} = \frac{21}{4} = 5\frac{1}{4}$$

d. 25

$$\frac{25}{6} \times \frac{6}{1} = \frac{150}{6} = 25$$

3.38 a

3.39 a

When $\frac{1}{2}$ is divided into seven equal parts, each part represents $\frac{1}{14}$.

3.40 c

When $\frac{1}{4}$ is divided into five equal parts, each part represents $\frac{1}{20}$.

3.41 c

When $\frac{1}{3}$ is divided into four equal parts, each part represents $\frac{1}{12}$.

3.42 b

When $\frac{1}{2}$ is divided into four equal parts, each part represents $\frac{1}{8}$.

3.43 d

Dividing by a proper fraction results in a quotient that is larger than the dividend.

3.44 d

When 6 is divided into thirds, there are 18 equal parts.

3.45 a

When 5 is divided into sixths, there are 30 equal parts.

3.46 a

When 1 is divided into fifths, there are 5 equal parts.

3.47 a

When 8 is divided into fourths, there are 32 equal parts.

3.48 b

3.49 b

3.50 a

3.51 b

SELF TEST 3

3.01 true

Multiplying by a proper fraction results in a smaller product.

3.02 true

Dividing by a proper fraction results in a larger quotient.

3.03 c

$$\frac{10}{3} \times \frac{8}{7} = \frac{80}{21} = 3\frac{17}{21}$$

3.04 b

When $\frac{1}{3}$ is divided into six equal parts, each part represents $\frac{1}{18}$.

3.05 a

$14 \div 7 = 2$
$2 \times 3 = 6$

3.06 d

$$\frac{1 \times 3}{9 \times 10} = \frac{3}{90} = \frac{1}{30}$$

3.07 c

When $\frac{1}{4}$ is divided into three equal parts, each part represents $\frac{1}{12}$.

3.08 b

Find $\frac{5}{11}$ of 22.

$22 \div 11 = 2$
$2 \times 5 = 10$

3.09 a

$$\frac{6}{5} \times \frac{3}{1} = \frac{18}{5} = 3\frac{3}{5}$$

3.010 b

3.011   c

To write a whole number as an improper fraction, write the whole number in the numerator and a 1 in the denominator.

3.012   12

$18 \div 3 = 6$
$6 \times 2 = 12$

3.013   24

When 6 is divided into fourths, there are 24 equal parts.

3.014 $\dfrac{15}{56}$

$\dfrac{3 \times 5}{8 \times 7} = \dfrac{15}{56}$

3.015 $1\dfrac{2}{15}$

$\dfrac{17}{6} \times \dfrac{2}{5} = \dfrac{24}{30} = 1\dfrac{4}{30} = 1\dfrac{2}{15}$

SECTION 4

4.1
  a. 7
  b. 2
  c. 4
  d. 3
  e. 8
  f. 9
  g. 6
  h. 5
  i. 1
  j. 10

4.2   a

$\dfrac{7}{8} - \dfrac{3}{8} = \dfrac{4}{8} = \dfrac{1}{2}$

4.3   b

$3\dfrac{4}{4} - 1\dfrac{1}{4} = 2\dfrac{3}{4}$

4.4   c

The LCD is 21.
$\dfrac{9}{21} + \dfrac{14}{21} = \dfrac{23}{21} = 1\dfrac{2}{21}$

4.5   c

$3 - \dfrac{1}{2} = 2\dfrac{1}{2}$

4.6   a

The LCD is 24.
$3\dfrac{3}{24} - \dfrac{14}{24} = 2\dfrac{27}{24} - \dfrac{14}{24} = 2\dfrac{13}{24}$

4.7   d

$24 \div 3 = 8$
$8 \times 2 = 16$

4.8   c

$\dfrac{5 \times 2}{6 \times 5} = \dfrac{10}{30} = \dfrac{1}{3}$

4.9   d
4.10 d

When 4 is divided evenly into thirds, there are 12 parts.

LIFEPAC TEST

1. false

To rewrite $7\frac{1}{15}$ by borrowing, subtract 1 from the whole number and add $\frac{15}{15}$ to the fraction. So, $7\frac{1}{15}$ is the same as $6\frac{16}{15}$.

2. true

4: 4, 8, 12, 16, 20, 24, 28, 32, **36**
9: 9, 18, 27, **36**

3. c

The LCD is 36.
$\frac{27}{36} + \frac{16}{36} = \frac{43}{36} = 1\frac{7}{36}$

4. b
5. d

Rewrite 3 as $2\frac{12}{12}$. Then, subtract.
$2\frac{12}{12} - 1\frac{5}{12} = 1\frac{7}{12}$

6. c

$7 - 4 = 3$

7. a

The LCD is 15.
$7\frac{1}{15} - 3\frac{12}{15} = 6\frac{16}{15} - 3\frac{12}{15} = 3\frac{4}{15}$

8. c

$2\frac{1}{2} + 5\frac{1}{2} = 8$

9. b

The LCD is 8.
$2\frac{4}{8} + 5\frac{5}{8} = 7\frac{9}{8} = 8\frac{1}{8}$

10. d

$36 \div 12 = 3$
$3 \times 7 = 21$

11. a

$32 \div 8 = 4$
$4 \times 5 = 20$

12. a

$\frac{7}{5} \times \frac{3}{1} = \frac{21}{5} = 4\frac{1}{5}$

13. d

$\frac{17}{8} \times \frac{13}{5} = \frac{221}{40} = 5\frac{21}{40}$

14. a

When 6 is divided into eighths, there are 48 equal parts.

15. d

When $\frac{1}{5}$ is divided evenly into four parts, each part represents $\frac{1}{20}$.

16. b

The LCD is 12.
$5\frac{9}{12} - 1\frac{5}{12} = 4\frac{4}{12} = 4\frac{1}{3}$

17. 8

$3\frac{1}{6} + 4\frac{5}{6} = 7\frac{6}{6} = 8$

18. $\frac{2}{5}$

$\frac{7}{10} - \frac{3}{10} = \frac{4}{10} = \frac{2}{5}$

19. $\frac{11}{18}$

The LCD is 18.
$\frac{15}{18} - \frac{4}{18} = \frac{11}{18}$

20. $\frac{15}{56}$

$\frac{3 \times 5}{8 \times 7} = \frac{15}{56}$

ALTERNATE LIFEPAC TEST

1. true
2. false

   5: 5, 10, 15, 20, 25, 30, 35, **40**
   8: 8, 16, 24, 32, **40**

3. b

   The LCD is 40.
   $\frac{24}{40} + \frac{25}{40} = \frac{49}{40} = 1\frac{9}{40}$

4. d
5. c

   Rewrite 4 as $3\frac{8}{8}$. Then, subtract.

   $3\frac{8}{8} - 2\frac{3}{8} = 1\frac{5}{8}$

6. d

   $8 - 2\frac{1}{2} = 5\frac{1}{2}$

7. a

   The LCD is 16.
   $8\frac{1}{16} - 2\frac{10}{16} = 7\frac{17}{16} - 2\frac{10}{16} = 5\frac{7}{16}$

8. d

   $5 + 3\frac{1}{2} = 8\frac{1}{2}$

9. b

   The LCD is 12.
   $4\frac{11}{12} + 3\frac{6}{12} = 7\frac{17}{12} = 8\frac{5}{12}$

10. a

    $24 \div 12 = 2$
    $2 \times 5 = 10$

11. c

    $32 \div 8 = 4$
    $4 \times 7 = 28$

12. b

    $\frac{8}{5} \times \frac{2}{1} = \frac{16}{5} = 3\frac{1}{5}$

13. c

    $\frac{15}{7} \times \frac{9}{2} = \frac{135}{14} = 9\frac{9}{14}$

14. b

    When 7 is divided into sixths, there are 42 equal parts.

15. d

    When $\frac{1}{8}$ is divided evenly into three parts, each part represents $\frac{1}{24}$.

16. a

    The LCD is 6.
    $6\frac{4}{6} - 3\frac{3}{6} = 3\frac{1}{6}$

17. 6

    $2\frac{5}{12} + 3\frac{7}{12} = 5\frac{12}{12} = 6$

18. $\frac{2}{3}$

    $\frac{5}{6} - \frac{1}{6} = \frac{4}{6} = \frac{2}{3}$

19. $\frac{19}{30}$

    The LCD is 30.
    $\frac{27}{30} - \frac{8}{30} = \frac{19}{30}$

20. $\frac{4}{15}$

    $\frac{2 \times 2}{5 \times 3} = \frac{4}{15}$

MATH 507

ALTERNATE LIFEPAC TEST

NAME _____

DATE _____

SCORE _____

$$\frac{80}{100}$$

Each numbered question = 5 points.

Answer *true* or *false*.

1. _____ $8\frac{1}{16}$ can be rewritten as $7\frac{17}{16}$.

2. _____ The LCD of $\frac{3}{5}$ and $\frac{5}{8}$ is 15.

Circle the correct letter and answer.

3. Add. Write your answer in simplest form. $\frac{3}{5} + \frac{5}{8}$

   a. $1\frac{4}{15}$ b. $1\frac{9}{40}$ c. $\frac{8}{13}$ d. $1\frac{1}{4}$

4. Add. Write your answer in simplest form. $\frac{3}{10} + \frac{4}{10}$

   a. $\frac{7}{20}$ b. $\frac{3}{5}$ c. $\frac{13}{14}$ d. $\frac{7}{10}$

5. Porter's family ordered 4 pizzas. They ate $2\frac{3}{8}$ of the pizzas. How much pizza is left?

   a. $2\frac{5}{8}$ pizzas   b. $2\frac{3}{8}$ pizzas   c. $1\frac{5}{8}$ pizzas   d. $1\frac{3}{8}$ pizzas

6. Estimate the difference by rounding each number to the nearest half or whole. $8\frac{1}{16} - 2\frac{5}{8}$

   a. $6\frac{1}{2}$ b. 6   c. 5   d. $5\frac{1}{2}$

7. Subtract. Write your answer in simplest form. $8\frac{1}{16} - 2\frac{5}{8}$

   a. $5\frac{7}{16}$ b. $6\frac{9}{16}$ c. $6\frac{1}{2}$ d. $5\frac{1}{16}$

8. Estimate the sum by rounding each number to the nearest half or whole. $4\frac{11}{12} + 3\frac{1}{2}$

   a. 9   b. $7\frac{1}{2}$ c. 8   d. $8\frac{1}{2}$

9. Find the sum. Write your answer in simplest form. $4\frac{11}{12} + 3\frac{1}{2}$

   a. $7\frac{6}{7}$ b. $8\frac{5}{12}$ c. $8\frac{1}{2}$ d. $8\frac{7}{12}$

10. Find $\frac{5}{12}$ of 24.

   a. 10   b. 15   c. 12   d. 20

11. The students in Nora's class chose between two options for an assignment. $\frac{7}{8}$ of the class chose option 1. If there are 32 students in Nora's class, how many chose option 1?

   a. 7   b. 21   c. 28   d. 30

12. Dean ran $1\frac{3}{5}$ miles. Sheila ran two times as far as Dean. How far did Sheila run?

   a. $2\frac{3}{5}$ miles   b. $3\frac{1}{5}$ miles   c. $2\frac{3}{10}$ miles   d. $2\frac{1}{5}$ miles

13. Multiply. Write your answer in simplest form. $2\frac{1}{7} \times 4\frac{1}{2}$

   a. $8\frac{1}{7}$ b. $12\frac{5}{14}$ c. $9\frac{9}{14}$ d. $8\frac{1}{14}$

14. Divide. Write your answer in simplest form. $7 \div \frac{1}{6}$

   a. $\frac{1}{20}$ b. 42   c. $\frac{6}{7}$ d. $1\frac{1}{6}$

15. Divide. Write your answer in simplest form. $\frac{1}{8} \div 3$

   a. 24   b. $\frac{3}{8}$ c. $2\frac{2}{3}$ d. $\frac{1}{24}$

16. Malcolm started with a board that was $6\frac{2}{3}$ feet long. He then cut off a section that was $3\frac{1}{2}$ feet long. How much of the board is left?

   a. $3\frac{1}{6}$ feet   b. 4 feet   c. $9\frac{3}{5}$ feet   d. $3\frac{1}{4}$ feet

Write the correct answer on the line.

17. Add. Write your answer in simplest form. $2\frac{5}{12} + 3\frac{7}{12}$ _____

18. Subtract. Write your answer in simplest form. $\frac{5}{6} - \frac{1}{6}$ _____

19. Subtract. Write your answer in simplest form. $\frac{9}{10} - \frac{4}{15}$ _____

20. Multiply. Write your answer in simplest form. $\frac{2}{5} \times \frac{2}{3}$ _____

MATH 508

Unit 8: Data Analysis and Probability

ANSWER KEYS

SECTION 1

1.1   a. 4
        b. 1
        c. 11
        d. 6
        e. 10
        f. 8
        g. 2
        h. 12
        i. 5
        j. 7
        k. 3
        l. 9

1.2   c

A random sample is needed for a valid conclusion.

1.3   c

Although 200 might give a clearer picture, it is not necessary to have that much data. Thirty should be enough.

1.4   d

Height is a quantity.

1.5   c

$2 + 15 + 8 + 2 = 27$

1.6   b

15 out of 27, well over half, are age 10.

1.7   c

There is not enough data because there is no clear conclusion.

1.8   b

$1 + 3 + 4 + 2 + 4 + 0 + 5 = 19$

1.9   b, d

Because the range will be wide, a table with intervals should be used.

1.10 a. 5
         b. 1
         c. 2
         d. 3
         e. 6
         f. 4

1.11 d

12 is the only data value that appears twice.

1.12 b

The middle pair is 8 and 10, and 9 is halfway between.

1.13 b

The numbers add to 54. $54 \div 6 = 9$

1.14 b

$12 - 5 = 7$

1.15 b

Because the range is wide, the mean may not be representative of the data, and/or there is probably not enough data to draw a valid conclusion.

1.16 c

Given only the extreme values, the only thing known for sure is the range.

1.17 b

$5 + 9 + 15 + 18 + 22 = 69$
$69 \div 5 = 13.8 \approx 14$

1.18 a

5 and 7 both occur twice.

1.19 a. 5
b. 2
c. 1
d. 4
e. 3

1.20 a. 1
b. 2

1.21 c

The mode is 8 because 8 occurs the most.

1.22 b

There are 10 ✘'s in the line plot.

1.23 b

The middle pair is 8 and 9, so 8.5 is the median.

1.24 a

The data values add to 84, and there are 10 data points.
84 ÷ 10 = 8.4 ≈ 8

1.25 a

5 is not with the clustered data.

1.26 b

There are 10 data points, in the correct columns.

1.27 a, b, c, d

Since the graph shows individual data, all the measures can be found.

1.28 c

Because there are 5 possible values, and there are 5 modes, each must have the same number of data points.

1.29 a. 2
b. 3
c. 5
d. 4
e. 1

1.30 a. 2
b. 1
c. 3

1.31 d

None of the values are repeated, so there is no mode.

1.32 a

There are 10 leaves.

1.33 b

The middle pair is 40 and 42, with 41 halfway between.

1.34 c

The sum of the data is 416, and there are 10 data points.
$\frac{416}{10} = 41.6 \approx 42$

1.35 c

The extreme values are 20 and 65
65 − 20 = 45

1.36 d

Because the range is wide, the mean often is not representative of the data.

1.37 a, c

Stem-and-leaf plots are useful for a wide range of data, displayed in intervals to show the shape of the data.

1.38 a

The graph has the correct number of data points (10), and the correct intervals (showing the gap at 40).

1.39 a. 3
b. 4
c. 2
d. 1
e. 5

SELF TEST 1

1.01   c

Age is a quantity.

1.02   d

The sample would be random and large enough.

1.03   b

2 + 10 + 8 + 7 = 27

1.04   c

There are eight tallies in the second row and four in the third row.

1.05   c

11 is the only data value that appears twice.

1.06   a

There are three numbers less than 8, and three numbers greater than 8.

1.07   a

The numbers add to 56.
56 ÷ 7 = 8

1.08   c

12 – 2 = 10

1.09   c

The middle pair is 5 and 6, and 5.5 is halfway between.

1.010   b

The data values add to 55, and there are 10 data points.
55 ÷ 10 = 5.5

1.011   c

9 is not with the clustered data.

1.012   a

Only a stem-and-leaf plot will show individual data for a wide range.

1.013   a

Three of the values are 60; the other values have only two or one.

1.014   c

The data values add to 620, and there are 9 values.
620 ÷ 9 ≈ 68.8 ≈ 69

1.015   d

There are four values below 70 and four at or above 70.

SECTION 2

2.1   a. 2
        b. 1

2.2   data

2.3   d

$9 + 3 + 5 + 3 + 1 = 21$

2.4   c

9 prefer math, 1 prefers history.
$9 - 1 = 8$

2.5   c

$3 + 5 + 3 = 11$

2.6   b

Math = 9, Writing = 3
$9 + 3 = 12$ $12 > \dfrac{21}{2}$

2.7   d

25 for each group:
5th: $6 + 8 + 6 + 5 = 25$
H.S.: $4 + 2 + 15 + 4 = 25$

2.8   b

$15 - 6 = 9$

2.9   d

$8 + 2 = 10$

2.10   d

$8 + 6 + 5 = 19$, or $25 - 6 = 19$

2.11   a. 2
         b. 3
         c. 1
         d. 4
         e. 5

2.12   a. 2
         b. 1

2.13   line graph

2.14   c, d

Line graphs compare two quantities, using data pairs.

2.15   c

Line graphs compare two quantities, usually showing a change over time.

2.16   a

The scores improve or stay the same each week.

2.17   c

The graph is steepest between week 3 and week 4.

2.18   c

The point above week 4 lines up with a score of 8.

2.19   d

The graph is flat between week 5 and 6, so there is no change in the score.

2.20   b

Because the plant is getting taller over time, the line would move upward.

2.21   a

The data must be plotted in the order that it occurs over time.

2.22   a. 3
         b. 1
         c. 5
         d. 2
         e. 4

2.23   a. 1
         b. 3
         c. 2

2.24   a

The data is categorical, so only a bar graph would be appropriate.

2.25   c

Only the line plot is used for numerical data and does not compare two variables.

2.26   a, c

> Each icon can represent as much categorical data as needed to make the graph fit in a given space.

2.27   d

> There are 8 dollar bill icons, each representing 2 million dollars.
> 8 × $2,000,000 = $16,000,000

2.28   a, b, d

> Only data for line graphs is given in numerical data pairs and shows change over time.

2.29   a, c, d
2.30   a, d

> A line plot can show continuous data and a line graph always does.

2.31   d

> Stem-and-leaf plots show what is typical, and show the data in intervals.

2.32   a. 4
             b. 1
             c. 3
             d. 2
             e. 5

SELF TEST 2

2.01   c

> 7 + 6 + 3 + 2 + 5 = 23

2.02   c

> Blonde = 7, Black = 6
> 7 + 6 = 13 $13 > \frac{23}{2}$

2.03   b

> 6 + 5 + 3 + 1 + 2 = 17

2.04   c

> 4 + 5 = 9

2.05   a, c

> The tallest bar will be the most common category. Adding the frequency of each bar will give the total number of data points.

2.06   b

> The amount of money goes down each weekend, except for one weekend where there is a slight increase.

2.07   b

> The graph is steepest between weekends 2 and 3.

2.08   c

> The graph is flat between weekends 3 and 4, so there is no change in the amount of money earned.

2.09   b

> If the point to the right is lower, the data value must have decreased.

2.010   c

> Line graphs compare two quantities, usually showing a change over time.

2.011 a

There are 24 dollar icons, each worth half a million dollars.
24 × 0.5 = 12 million dollars

2.012 c

There are 14 dollar icons (8 for education, 6 for prisons), each worth half a million dollars.
14 × 0.5 = 7 million dollars

2.013 c

The graph is looking at change in profit over time, so only a line graph would be appropriate.

2.014 c

A bar graph is used for categorical data, especially with a relatively small data set.

2.015 a, c

Continuous data can have any value within a range and are used in line graphs.

SECTION 3

3.1
  a. 3
  b. 4
  c. 2
  d. 1

3.2 c

While we could argue about the likelihood of each event, it is certain the sun will rise.

3.3 d

A game is not fair if there is not an equal chance of winning as not winning.

3.4 c

If there are an equal number of each color marble, each is equally likely to be drawn.

3.5 c

Spinner C is closest to equally fair.

3.6 b

There are 10 odd numbers and 10 even numbers on the spinner.

3.7 d

There are more than twice as many girls as boys.

3.8 b

Although the chances of winning are equally likely as unlikely, this spinner has the most red sections.

3.9 b

Because there are as many ways to win as lose, the game/event is fair.

3.10 a, c

Events can be certain or impossible, depending on the outcomes.

3.11   a. you win the lottery
            b. you will be sick next week
            c. your favorite team will win
            d. you will go to school Monday
            e. the sun will rise

3.12   a. 24 red, 1 blue
            b. 15 red, 10 blue
            c. 13 red, 12 blue
            d. 10 red, 15 blue
            e. 1 red, 24 blue

3.13   a. 2
            b. 1
            c. 3

3.14   c

$$\frac{8}{24} = \frac{1}{3}$$

3.15   c

There are 6 multiples of 3: 3, 6, 9, 12, 15, and 18.

$$\frac{6}{20} = \frac{3}{10}$$

3.16   a

1 number out of 8 is a favorable outcome.

3.17   b

Probability cannot be > 1.

3.18   a

$$\frac{6 \text{ red}}{(6 \text{ red} + 24 \text{ blue})} = \frac{6}{30} = \frac{1}{5} \qquad \frac{1}{5} < \frac{1}{4}$$

3.19   c

$$\frac{6 \text{ hearts}}{(6 \text{ hearts} + 4 \text{ clubs} + 8 \text{ spades})} = \frac{6}{18} = \frac{1}{3}$$

3.20   a, b, c

Adding a star to a blank card gives $\frac{5}{10}$ or $\frac{1}{2}$ probability.

Adding 2 "star" cards gives $\frac{6}{12}$ or $\frac{1}{2}$ probability.

Taking away 2 blank cards gives $\frac{4}{8}$ or $\frac{1}{2}$ probability.

3.21   a

The ratios are: $\frac{1}{2}, \frac{1}{3}, \frac{1}{10}$, and $\frac{2}{5}$, with $\frac{1}{2}$ being the largest.

3.22   a. draw a number greater than 100
            b. draw a multiple of 25
            c. draw a multiple of 10
            d. draw an even number
            e. draw a number less then 100

3.23   a. draw a 2-digit number
            b. draw a multiple of 3
            c. draw a number ending in 0 or 5
            d. draw a number ending in 7
            e. draw the number 37

3.24   a. 4
            b. 3
            c. 2
            d. 1

3.25   c

There are four possible outcomes: HT, HH, TH, TT. Only heads/heads is favorable.

3.26   c

There are four possible outcomes.

3.27   c

There are twelve possible outcomes, and three are favorable (1-1, 2-2, 3-3).

$$\frac{3}{12} = \frac{1}{4}$$

3.28   d

There are twelve possible outcomes, and six are favorable (1-4, 2-3, 2-4, 3-2, 3-3, 3-4).

$$\frac{6}{12} = \frac{1}{2}$$

3.29   c

There are four possible outcomes for the first event, or branch: 1, 2, 3, and 4.

3.30   b

There are two possible outcomes for the event, or branch: A and B.

3.31 d

There are eight possible outcomes for the event: 1A, 1B, 2A, 2B, 3A, 3B, 4A, and 4B.

3.32 b

There are forty possible outcomes for the event. Heads will be paired with each of the twenty numbers, and tails will be paired with each of the twenty numbers, for a total of forty possible outcomes.

3.33 a. 3
b. 2
c. 1
d. 4
e. 5

3.34 a. 3
b. 2
c. 1

3.35 d

There are four possible outcomes: HT, HH, TH, TT. Two out of four are favorable, so half of the results should be matching.

3.36 b

$$\frac{1}{20} = \frac{x}{300} \qquad \frac{1}{20} \times \frac{15}{15} = \frac{15}{300}$$
Or, $300 \div 20 = 15$

3.37 b

There are twelve outcomes, and one is favorable.
$$\frac{1}{12} = \frac{x}{600} \qquad \frac{1}{12} \times \frac{50}{50} = \frac{50}{600}$$
Or, $600 \div 12 = 50$

3.38 d

Half of the flips should be tails, so if half of the flips is 400, there are 800 total flips (400 × 2 = 800).

3.39 d

$$\frac{3}{5} = \frac{x}{400} \qquad \frac{3}{5} \times \frac{80}{80} = \frac{240}{400}$$

3.40 c

$$\frac{1}{5} = \frac{x}{375} \qquad \frac{1}{5} \times \frac{75}{75} = \frac{75}{375}$$
Or, $375 \div 5 = 75$

3.41 b

The ratio of the expected results must be equal to the theoretical probability.
$$\frac{5}{40} \div \frac{5}{5} = \frac{1}{8}$$

3.42 b

Because the theoretical probability is known, it should be used. Ten trials is not enough to predict reliably.
The probability of getting a 3 is $\frac{1}{6}$.
$$\frac{1}{6} = \frac{x}{240} \qquad \frac{1}{6} \times \frac{40}{40} = \frac{40}{240}$$
Or, $240 \div 6 = 40$

3.43 b

3.44 a. 2
b. 1
c. 4
d. 5
e. 3

SELF TEST 3

3.01 d

> None of the numbers is a multiple of 25.

3.02 b

> There will be as many ways to win as lose, which is a fair game.

3.03 c

> Event C is closest to the middle.

3.04 c

> $\dfrac{8}{32} = \dfrac{1}{4}$

3.05 b

> There are four multiples of 5: 5, 10, 15, and 20.
>
> $\dfrac{4}{20} = \dfrac{1}{5}$

3.06 d

> $\dfrac{15 \text{ blue}}{(5 \text{ red} + 15 \text{ blue})} = \dfrac{15}{20} = \dfrac{3}{4}$

3.07 b

> $\dfrac{6 \text{ hearts}}{(6 \text{ hearts} + 12 \text{ clubs} + 6 \text{ diamonds})} = \dfrac{6}{24} = \dfrac{1}{4}$

3.08 d

> The 100 outcomes for the spinner will be paired with heads and tails, for a total of 200 possible outcomes.

3.09 b

> There are twelve possible outcomes for the event, and only two (C1 and C3) are favorable.
>
> $\dfrac{2}{12} = \dfrac{1}{6}$

3.010 b

> There are sixteen possible outcomes: H1 through H8, and T1 through T8. Only T2 and T1 are favorable outcomes.
>
> $\dfrac{2}{16} = \dfrac{1}{8}$

3.011 c

> There are sixteen possible outcomes, and three are favorable (1-7, 2-6, and 3-5).
>
> $\dfrac{3}{16}$

3.012 c

> The ratio of the expected results must be equal to the theoretical probability:
>
> $\dfrac{4}{60} \div \dfrac{4}{4} = \dfrac{1}{15}$

3.013 d

> There are six outcomes, and three are favorable.
>
> $\dfrac{3}{6} = \dfrac{1}{2} = \dfrac{x}{200}$ $\dfrac{1}{2} \times \dfrac{100}{100} = \dfrac{100}{200}$
>
> Or, $200 \div 2 = 100$

3.014 d

> Two out of every eight spins should be a number less than 3, so if $\dfrac{1}{4}$ of the spins is 80, there are 320 spins ($80 \times 4 = 320$).

3.015 c

> $\dfrac{3}{9} = \dfrac{1}{3} = \dfrac{x}{33}$ $\dfrac{1}{3} \times \dfrac{11}{11} = \dfrac{11}{33}$
>
> Or, $33 \div 3 = 11$

SECTION 4

4.1   a. 17
        b. 3
        c. 8
        d. 6
        e. 13
        f. 12
        g. 1
        h. 5
        i. 16
        j. 11
        k. 15
        l. 7
        m. 4
        n. 2
        o. 9
        p. 10
        q. 14

4.2   d

$$5 + 6 + 7 + 4 = 22$$

4.3   b

$$\frac{(6 + 7 + 9 + 10 + 11)}{6} = \frac{54}{6} = 9$$

4.4   d

The 9 column is the tallest.

4.5   b

4.6   b

Seven men preferred action movies, but only two women did.

4.7   a

The graph is steepest between weeks 1 and 2.

4.8   a

The data is categorical and discrete.

4.9   b

With only one possibility out of 10, it is unlikely.

4.10   c

There are five vowels out of twenty-six letters.

4.11   d

There are six favorable outcomes (1-1, 2-2, 3-3, 4-4, 5-5, 6-6) out of thirty-six total outcomes.

$$\frac{6}{36} = \frac{1}{6}$$

4.12   b

Eight out of twenty-four cards, or $\frac{1}{3}$, are diamonds.

$$\frac{1}{3} = \frac{100}{300}$$

4.13   c

There are twelve outcomes, and three are favorable (T-2, T-4, and T-6).

$$\frac{3}{12} = \frac{1}{4}$$

LIFEPAC TEST

1.   c

A random sample is needed for a valid conclusion.

2.   d

$4 + 11 + 10 + 2 = 27$

3.   c

The middle pair is 9 and 11, and 10 is halfway between.

4.   d

13 is the only data point that occurs twice.

5.   a

The data values add to 30.
$30 \div 10 = 3$

6.   d

The extreme values are 0 and 6.
$6 - 0 = 6$

7.   c

90 occurs four times, once more than 85.

8.   c

There are twenty-four leaves.

9.   d

$6 + 6 = 12$

10.   d

Only three people prefer science fiction.

11.   b

The sales are less each week except for one.

12.   a

The graph is steepest between weeks 1 and 2.

13.   b

The graph will show change over time.

14.   c

A line plot uses numerical data, and shows individual data.

15.   a

It is very likely, but not certain that a blue marble will be chosen.

16.   c

$$\frac{8 \text{ green}}{(6 \text{ red} + 4 \text{ blue} + 8 \text{ green})} = \frac{8}{18} = \frac{4}{9}$$

17.   c

There are twelve outcomes, and nine are favorable: 1-1, 1-2, 1-3, 1-4, 2-1, 2-2, 2-3, 3-1, and 3-2.
$$\frac{9}{12} = \frac{3}{4}$$

18.   d

There are nine outcomes, and all nine are favorable.
$$\frac{9}{9} = 1$$

19.   b

The ratio of the expected results must be equal to the theoretical probability:
$$\frac{6}{180} \div \frac{6}{6} = \frac{1}{30}$$

20.   d

$$\frac{12}{25} = \frac{x}{300} \qquad \frac{12}{25} \times \frac{12}{12} = \frac{144}{300}$$

ALTERNATE LIFEPAC TEST

1. d

A random sample is needed for a valid conclusion.

2. b

2 + 11 + 6 + 1 = 20

3. a

The extreme values are 5 and 16.
16 – 5 = 11

4. c

The middle pair is 12 and 14. 13 is halfway between them.

5. a

The data values add to 40.
40 ÷ 10 = 4

6. b

5 is the tallest column.

7. c

The middle pair is 85 and 86. 85.5 is halfway between.

8. d

99 occurs three times, once more than three other values.

9. d

6 + 4 = 10

10. b

Seven women prefer romance, and only one man does.

11. c

The sales are staying around 70.

12. d

The graph is steepest between weeks 5 and 6.

13. c

A line plot shows the shape of the data and what is typical.

14. a

A line graph is the only graph that uses data pairs.

15. c

While there is only one way to draw the correct card, it is not impossible.

16. b

$$\frac{4 \text{ green}}{(8 \text{ red} + 12 \text{ blue} + 4 \text{ green})} = \frac{4}{24} = \frac{1}{6}$$

17. d

It is not possible to get a total of more than 7.

18. c

There are nine outcomes, and three are favorable (10-3, 11-2, and 12-1).

$$\frac{3}{9} = \frac{1}{3}$$

19. c

The ratio of the expected results must be equal to the theoretical probability:

$$\frac{12}{60} \div \frac{12}{12} = \frac{1}{5}$$

20. d

$$\frac{3}{25} = \frac{x}{350} \qquad \frac{3}{25} \times \frac{14}{14} = \frac{42}{350}$$

MATH 508

ALTERNATE LIFEPAC TEST

NAME _____

DATE _____

SCORE _____

80

100

Each numbered question = 5 points

Circle the correct letter and answer.

1. Which example would be likely to give a valid conclusion?
    a. Eight students are surveyed about their favorite movie.
    b. People are asked, "Do you like yucky vegetarian food, or juicy burgers?"
    c. Six swimmers are asked if they like the water.
    d. The first thirty people to leave the library are asked their age.

2. How many people were in the survey shown in this frequency table?
    a. 4
    b. 20
    c. 26
    d. 30

AGE OF PEOPLE AT BILLY'S BIRTHDAY PARTY		
AGE	TALLIES	FREQUENCY
5	||	2
6	ⵀⵀ ⵀⵀ |	11
7	ⵀⵀ |	6
8	|	1

3. What is the range for the following set of data?   5, 7, 12, 14, 16, 16
    a. 11   b. 12   c. 13   d. 14

4. What is the median for the following set of data?   5, 7, 12, 14, 16, 16
    a. 11.7   b. 12   c. 13   d. 14

5. What is the mean for the Quiz Scores?
   a. 4
   b. 5
   c. 6
   d. 7

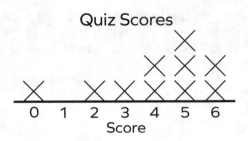

Quiz Scores

6. What is the mode for the set of data from Question 5?
   a. 4   b. 5   c. 6   d. 7

7. What is the median of the Math Test Scores?
   a. 49
   b. 85
   c. 85.5
   d. 86

Math Test Scores

```
5 | 0  5
6 | 4  5  7
7 | 5  8  8
8 | 2  4  5  6  7  7
9 | 0  1  2  3  3  9  9  9
```

5 | 0 = 50

8. What is the mode of the data set from Question 7?
   a. 58   b. 87
   c. 93   d. 99

9. According to the Favorite Book bar graph, how many people altogether like non-fiction?
   a. 3
   b. 6
   c. 8
   d. 10

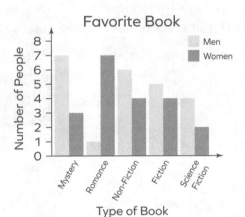

Favorite Book

10. According to the bar graph from Question 9, what type of book do women prefer much more than men?
    a. mystery   b. romance
    c. fiction   d. science fiction

11. According to the Store Sales graph, how would you describe the store sales overall?

Store Sales

a. increasing

b. decreasing

c. staying the same

d. can't be determined

12. According to the graph from Question 11, where is the greatest change in the store sales?

a. from week 1 to week 2

b. from week 2 to week 3

c. from week 3 to week 4

d. from week 5 to week 6

13. What type of graph would have the title "Typical Height Jumped"?

a. line graph   b. bar graph   c. line plot   d. pictograph

14. If you had a set of data pairs that show the amount of rain for each month of the year, what type of graph should you use?

a. line graph   b. bar graph   c. line plot   d. pictograph

15. What is the likelihood that you would randomly draw the 3 of hearts from a deck of 52 playing cards?

a. likely   b. equally likely as unlikely

c. unlikely   d. certain

16. In a bag there are eight red marbles, twelve blue marbles, and four green marbles. What is the probability that you will draw a green marble?

a. $\frac{1}{12}$ b. $\frac{1}{6}$ c. $\frac{1}{4}$ d. $\frac{1}{3}$

17. If the two spinners below are spun, what is the probability that the numbers will add to more than 7?

a. $\frac{1}{12}$

b. $\frac{1}{6}$

c. $\frac{1}{4}$

d. 0

18. Here is a tree diagram showing the sample space for two independent events. What is the probability of getting a total of 13?

    a. $\frac{1}{9}$

    b. $\frac{2}{9}$

    c. $\frac{1}{3}$

    d. $\frac{2}{3}$

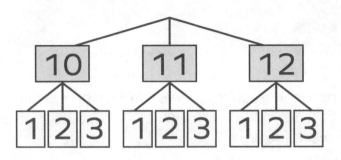

19. For a certain experiment, if we expect to get a red marble twelve times in 60 trials, what is the theoretical probability of getting a red marble?

    a. $\frac{1}{12}$ b. $\frac{1}{10}$ c. $\frac{1}{5}$ d. $\frac{1}{4}$

20. In a class experiment, Debra finds that the probability that a student has more than three siblings is $\frac{3}{25}$. If the school population is 350, how many students would we expect to have more than three siblings, based on Debra's experiment?

    a. 15   b. 25   c. 35   d. 42

MATH 509

Unit 9: Geometry

ANSWER KEYS

SECTION 1

1.1   a. 10
         b. 5
         c. 2
         d. 3
         e. 7
         f. 9
         g. 8
         h. 6
         i. 1
         j. 4

1.2   b, c

> Planes are two-dimensional.

1.3   a, d

> Three letters or a number are needed to name the angle.

1.4   a, d

> Parallel lines do not intersect.

1.5   a, b

> Two points on a line can define a ray or a line segment.

1.6   a, c, d

> The correct notation must be used and only connected points can be considered.

1.7   b, c, d

> The correct notation must be used and only connected points can be considered.

1.8   b, c, d

> The correct notation must be used and only connected points can be considered.

1.9   b, d

> The correct notation must be used and only connected points can be considered.

1.10

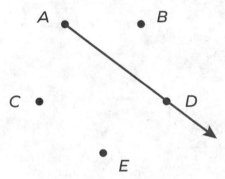

1.11

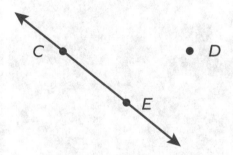

1.12

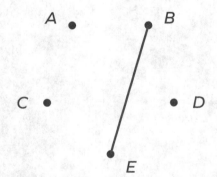

1.13

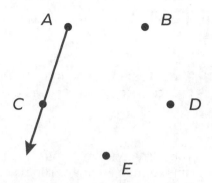

1.14

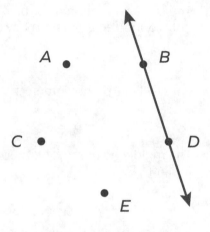

1.15

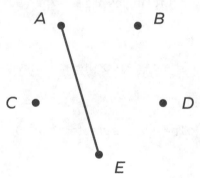

1.16   a. 5
         b. 3
         c. 7
         d. 6
         e. 1
         f. 4
         g. 2
1.17   b

Acute angles are less than 90°.

1.18   a

Obtuse angles are greater than 90°.

1.19   a, b, c

Perpendicular lines meet at 90°, which are right angles.

1.20   a, d

90° is a right angle, and 180° is a straight angle.

1.21   d

Acute angles are less than 90°.

1.22   b

The angle is less than 90°.

1.23   b, d

70° is an acute angle, but it can be measured opening from the left or right.

1.24   b

The angle is acute and close to 90.

1.25   a. 2
         b. 1
         c. 5
         d. 3
         e. 4
1.26   b, c

A radius has one endpoint on the circle and the other at the center.

1.27   a, b

A chord has both endpoints on the circle. A diameter is a chord.

1.28   b

A diameter is a chord that passes through the center.

1.29 c

The larger the radius, the larger the circumference.

1.30 c

The diameter is twice the radius.

1.31 b

The radius is half the diameter.

1.32 c

A diameter is a chord, and it is the longest since it passes through the center.

1.33 a, b, c, d

Any line segment can be measured; the circumference can be measured as well.

1.34
a. 5
b. 4
c. 3
d. 2
e. 1

SELF TEST 1

1.01 a, c, d

The correct notation must be used, and only connected points can be considered.

1.02 b, d, e

The correct notation must be used, and only connected points can be considered.

1.03 a, c, e

The correct notation must be used, and only connected points can be considered.

1.04 b, c

Parallel lines do not intersect.

1.05 b, c

The middle point must be the vertex (point D, E, H, or I).

1.06 b

Acute angles are less than 90°.

1.07 b

The angle is acute and halfway to 90°.

1.08 d

The angle is greater than 90°, and close to 180°.

1.09 c

Obtuse angles measure greater than 90°.

1.010 b

If the angle is obtuse, it must be greater than 90°.

1.011 a, d

A radius has one endpoint on the circle and the other at the center.

1.012 a, c, d

A chord has both endpoints on the circle. A diameter is a chord.

1.013 d

A diameter is a chord that passes through the center.

1.014 c

The larger the larger the circumference, the larger the radius.

1.015 a

The radius is half the diameter.

SECTION 2

2.1
a. 8
b. 9
c. 11
d. 1
e. 10
f. 6
g. 5
h. 4
i. 2
j. 3
k. 7

2.2 b

"oct-" means "eight," so an octagon has 8 sides

2.3 b

"hept-" means "seven," so a heptagon has 7 sides

2.4 a

"hex-" means "six," so a hexagon has 6 sides and 6 angles

2.5 a

A 20-gon has 20 sides, more than the others.

2.6 d

The figure must be closed (sides can't cross) and made of line segments.

2.7 c

An octagon has 8 sides. The other polygons have more sides (10, 9, and 12).

2.8 c

If the polygon is regular, each side is the same length.

2.9 b

All of the polygons are regular, except one.

2.10   d

> A regular polygon has sides of the same length and angles of the same measure. A rhombus is not a regular polygon.

2.11   a

> This is part of the definition of a regular polygon.

2.12   a. 1
        b. 5
        c. 2
        d. 4
        e. 3

2.13   a. 3
        b. 2
        c. 4
        d. 1
        e. 5
        f. 6

2.14   a, b, c, d

> Any triangle will have at least one acute angle.

2.15   b, d

> The triangle has an obtuse angle, and two sides that are the same length.

2.16   b, c

> None of the sides or two of the sides of a triangle can be the same length and still be obtuse.

2.17   a, d

> The triangle has an obtuse angle, and none of the sides are the same length.

2.18   b, d

> The triangle has acute angles, and two of the sides are the same length.

2.19   b

> All sides of a regular polygon are the same length.

2.20   a, c

> An equilateral triangle is considered isosceles and will always be acute.

2.21   b, c

> The triangle has a right angle, and two of the sides are the same length.

2.22   a. 6
        b. 2
        c. 5
        d. 1
        e. 4
        f. 3

2.23   a, d

> All isosceles trapezoids are trapezoids.

2.24   b, c

> By definition, a rhombus has four sides of the same length. A square is a rhombus.

2.25   b, c

> By definition, a rectangle has right angles.

2.26   c, d

> Quadrilaterals and trapezoids are not parallelograms.

2.27   a, b

> A square is a type of rectangle, and rectangles are a type of parallelogram.

2.28   c, d

> All rhombuses are parallelograms.

2.29   c

> A parallelogram with four right angles is a rectangle.

2.30   d

> A rectangle has four right angles, and a rhombus has four sides of the same length. Both are properties of a square.

2.31 a. 1
b. 2
c. 3
d. 4
e. 5

2.32 a. 13
b. 12
c. 5
d. 8
e. 10
f. 6
g. 1
h. 2
i. 7
j. 11
k. 4
l. 14
m. 9
n. 15
o. 3

2.33 b

The top and bottom are rectangles, as are the lateral faces.

2.34 a, c

The base of a prism can be any polygon. The lateral faces will be congruent only if the base is a regular polygon.

2.35 b

A rectangular prism has twelve edges and six faces.

2.36 c

There are four vertices at the base, and one at the top. Similarly, there is the base and four faces for each side of the base.

2.37 c

This is a pyramid with a square base.

2.38 b

There are six rectangular faces.

2.39 a

A cylinder has a lateral surface.

2.40 d

There are two circular bases, so this is a cylinder.

2.41 a

SELF TEST 2

2.01 c

Polygons beyond 12 sides are named with the number of sides.

2.02 b

"quad-" means "four," so a quadrilateral has four sides

2.03 c

"do-" means "two" and "deca-" means "ten," so a dodecagon has 12 sides (2 and 10)

2.04 a

Only one polygon is irregular.

2.05 a

The triangle has a right angle and two sides that are the same length.

2.06 c, d

A right triangle can have none or two sides the same length.

2.07 a, b, d

An isosceles triangle can be acute, and an equilateral triangle is isosceles.

2.08 a, d

The triangle has an obtuse angle and none of the sides are the same length.

2.09 a, d

By definition an isosceles trapezoid has two congruent sides. A quadrilateral could have as many as three congruent sides.

2.010 a, b

Rhombuses are parallelograms with four congruent sides.

2.011 b

The figure has two sets of parallel sides.

2.012 d

There is one square base and four triangular faces.

2.013 b

The top and bottom are rectangles, as are the lateral faces.

2.014 c

There are four edges at the base, and four between the lateral faces.

2.015 d

A cone has one circular base.

SECTION 3

3.1   a. 2
        b. 4
        c. 1
        d. 3
        e. 5

3.2   c

Vertex *C* corresponds to vertex *G*.

3.3   d

Vertex *D* corresponds to vertex *H*, and vertex *A* to vertex *E*.

3.4   a

Corresponding angles of similar triangles are congruent.

3.5   d

Corresponding angles of similar triangles are congruent.

3.6   c

Corresponding angles of similar triangles are congruent.

3.7   c

The sides of *ABCD* are twice as long as the sides of *EFGH*. The ratio of *GH* to *CD* is 3 to 6, or 1 to 2.

3.8   c

The sides of *ABCD* are twice as long as the sides of *EFGH*. The ratio of *GH* to *CD* is 3 to 6, or 1 to 2.

3.9   a

The sides of *ABCD* are twice as long as the sides of *EFGH*. The ratio of *GH* to *CD* is 3 to 6, or 1 to 2.

3.10   c

Congruent figures are the same shape and size.

3.11   a, c, d

Congruent figures have congruent corresponding parts, so the ratio of corresponding sides is 1 to 1.

3.12   a. 3
         b. 2
         c. 5
         d. 4
         e. 1
         f. 6
         g. 8
         h. 7

3.13   a. 4
         b. 6
         c. 1
         d. 5
         e. 2
         f. 3
         g. 7

3.14   d

△4 is translated down 3 units.

3.15   a

△1 is reflected over a vertical line.

3.16   c

△3 is rotated 180°.

3.17   a, c

Translations, reflections, and rotations produce congruent images.

3.18   a

The vertices match a translation.

3.19   b

The vertices match a reflection over a vertical line.

3.20   c

The vertices match a rotation of 180°.

3.21   c

The triangle is rotated 90°.

3.22   a. 3
       b. 1
       c. 2

3.23   b

There would be one line of symmetry from the top vertex to the midpoint of the opposite side.

3.24   c

A parallelogram does not have line symmetry.

3.25   a

There is a vertical line through the 0 and a horizontal line through each digit.

3.26   d

There would be two lines of symmetry; one from each vertex to the opposite vertex. There would be two more from each side midpoint to the opposite side midpoint. The figure is a square.

3.27   b

The two halves are reflections of each other.

3.28   b

619 can be rotated 180 degrees around a point in the center of 1.

3.29   d

The hexagon has point symmetry (180°), but not line symmetry.

3.30   c

There is a vertical and horizontal line of symmetry, and the rhombus has point symmetry (180°).

3.31

	Line Sym.	Point Sym.	Neither
a.	C		
b.		Z	
c.	M		
d.			J
e.			P
f.		N	
g.		S	
h.	D		
i.			F

SELF TEST 3

3.01 a

> Corresponding angles of similar triangles are congruent.

3.02 b

> The sides of $\triangle DEF$ are four times as long as the sides of $\triangle ABC$. The ratio of BC to EF is 5 to 20, or 1 to 4.

3.03 b

> Corresponding angles of similar triangles are congruent.

3.04 c

> The sides of $\triangle DEF$ are four times as long as the sides of $\triangle ABC$. The ratio of BC to EF is 5 to 20, or 1 to 4.

3.05 d

> Congruent figures are the same shape and size.

3.06 d

> $\triangle 4$ is reflected over a horizontal line.

3.07 a

> $\triangle 3$ is rotated 90°.

3.08 c

> $\triangle 2$ and $\triangle 3$ are translations: a transformation in which a figure is slid to a new location.

3.09 a

> The triangle is translated 3 units to the right.

3.010 d

> Because the vertices are not labeled, this could be any of the three transformations.

3.011 a

> There is a horizontal line of symmetry.

3.012 d

> The two halves are reflections of each other.

3.013 a

> There is a vertical and horizontal line of symmetry.

3.014 c

> Both halves must be reflections of each other.

3.015 d

> A square can be rotated 90° and has four lines of symmetry.

SECTION 4

4.1   a. 3
        b. 1
        c. 2

4.2   c

The correct notation must be used and only connected points can be considered.

4.3   c

The angle is obtuse and getting towards 180°.

4.4   c

The diameter is twice the radius.

4.5   d

"non-" means "nine," so a nonagon has nine sides and nine angles

4.6   a

There is one pair of parallel sides.

4.7   d

The net has triangular bases and rectangular faces.

4.8   a

There is one base and one face for each side of the base.

4.9   d

An angle greater than 90° is obtuse, and two congruent sides is isosceles.

4.10   d

The sides of *ABCD* are twice as long as the sides of *EFGH*. The ratio of *EH* to *AD* is 4 to 8, or 1 to 2.

4.11   b

Corresponding angles of similar triangles are congruent.

4.12   c

The quadrilateral is rotated 90°.

4.13   b

The two halves are reflections of each other.

LIFEPAC TEST

1. a

    The correct notation must be used and only connected points can be considered.

2. d

    The correct notation must be used and only connected points can be considered.

3. b

    The vertex of the angle must be the middle letter.

4. d

    The angle forms a straight line.

5. c

    The radius is half the diameter.

6. a

    A chord has both endpoints on the circle.

7. b

    The polygon has eight sides.

8. a

    If the polygon is regular, each side is the same length.

9. c

    One angle measure is greater than 90°.

10. c, d

    There is a right angle and none of the sides are the same length.

11. a

    A trapezoid has one pair of parallel sides.

12. b

    There are two pairs of parallel sides.

13. b

    The top and bottom are rectangles, as are the lateral faces.

14. a

    There are four vertices on each base.

15. b

    Corresponding angles of congruent triangles are congruent.

16. c

    Similar figures are the same shape, but not necessarily the same size.

17. a

    The trapezoid is translated two units to the right.

18. d

    △4 is reflected over a vertical line.

19. c

    There are five lines of symmetry from each tip to the opposite indent.

20. b

    The two halves are reflections of each other.

ALTERNATE LIFEPAC TEST

1. c

   The correct notation must be used and only connected points can be considered.

2. d

   The correct notation must be used and only connected points can be considered.

3. c

   The vertex of the angle must be the middle letter.

4. a

   The angle is less than 90°.

5. a

   The radius is half the diameter.

6. b

   A diameter is a chord that passes through the center.

7. b

   The polygon has eight sides.

8. b

   If the polygon is regular, each side is the same length.

9. b

   There is a right angle (90°).

10. a, d

    The triangle has an obtuse angle and none of the sides are the same length.

11. c

    A parallelogram has two pairs of parallel sides.

12. d

    The sides of the trapezoid are congruent, while the bases are parallel.

13. b

    There are two circular bases.

14. b

    There are four edges around each base, and four more between each lateral face.

15. a

    Corresponding sides of congruent triangles are congruent.

16. d

    Similar figures are the same shape, but not necessarily the same size.

17. c

    The trapezoid is rotated 180° around the upper right vertex.

18. b

    △2 is translated six units up.

19. d

    There would be a vertical and horizontal line of symmetry and two diagonal lines.

20. d

    The two halves are reflections of each other.

MATH 509

ALTERNATE LIFEPAC TEST

NAME _____

DATE _____

SCORE _____

80 / 100

Each numbered question = 5 points

Circle the correct letter and answer.

1. Which of the following is a line segment shown in this drawing?

    a. $\overleftrightarrow{AB}$

    b. $\overline{AE}$

    c. $\overline{BE}$

    d. $\overleftrightarrow{DE}$

2. Which of the following is a ray shown in the drawing from Question 1?

    a. $\overrightarrow{AD}$ b. $\overleftrightarrow{AC}$ c. $\overrightarrow{CE}$ d. $\overrightarrow{AB}$

3. Which of the following is an angle shown in the drawing from Question 1?

    a. ∠EBD b. ∠FBA c. ∠BEF d. ∠CED

4. What type of angle is shown here?

    a. acute

    b. obtuse

    c. right

    d. straight

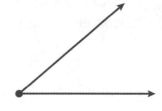

5. What is the radius of ⊙C?

    a. 8.5 cm

    b. 9 cm

    c. 17 cm

    d. 34 cm

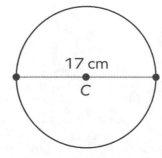

17 cm

C

6. Which line segment is a diameter of ⊙F?
   a. $\overline{AB}$
   b. $\overline{EC}$
   c. $\overline{DF}$
   d. $\overline{FC}$

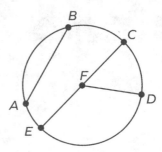

7. What polygon is shown here?
   a. hexagon
   b. pentagon
   c. octagon
   d. decagon

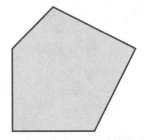

8. If one side of a regular hexagon is 3 cm, how long is each of the other sides?
   a. 2 cm   b. 3 cm   c. 6 cm   d. 18 cm

9. The angle measures in a triangle are 40°, 90°, and 50°. What type of triangle is it?
   a. acute triangle   b. right triangle   c. obtuse triangle   d. isosceles triangle

10. What type of triangle is shown here? (There may be more than one correct answer.)
    a. scalene triangle   b. isosceles triangle
    c. right triangle   d. obtuse triangle

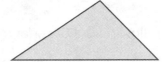

11. What is the most specific name for a quadrilateral with two pairs of parallel sides?
    a. trapezoid   b. rectangle   c. parallelogram   d. quadrilateral

12. What the most specific name for the quadrilateral shown here?
    a. trapezoid   b. parallelogram
    c. square   d. isosceles trapezoid

13. What solid figure is shown here?
    a. cone
    b. cylinder
    c. triangular prism
    d. rectangular prism

14. What solid figure has 12 edges?
    a. triangular pyramid
    b. rectangular prism
    c. square pyramid
    d. triangular prism

15. In the congruent triangles shown here, what is the length of $\overline{DE}$?
    a. 3 cm
    b. 4 cm
    c. 5 cm
    d. 6 cm

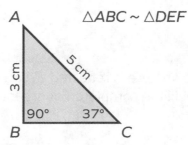 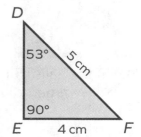

$\triangle ABC \sim \triangle DEF$

16. Which of the figures shown here are similar?
    a. 3 and 4
    b. 2 and 3
    c. 1 and 4
    d. 1 and 3

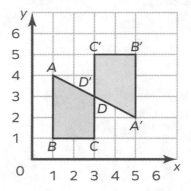

17. What transformation is shown here?
    a. translation
    b. reflection
    c. rotation
    d. can't be determined

18. Which triangle is a translation of triangle A?
    a. △1
    b. △2
    c. △3
    d. △4

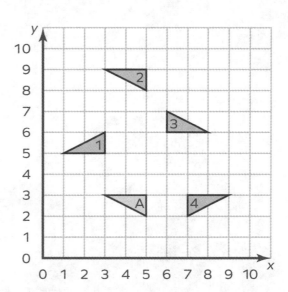

19. How many lines of symmetry does this figure have?
   a. 1
   b. 2
   c. 3
   d. 4

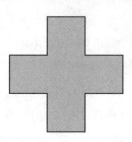

20. If the half-figure shown here is reflected over the line of symmetry, what will the completed figure look like?

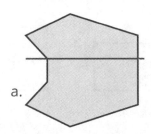 a.

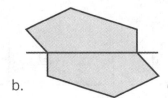 b.

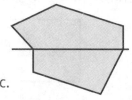 c.

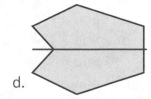 d.

MATH 510

Unit 10: Perimeter, Area, and Volume

ANSWER KEYS

SECTION 1

1.1   perimeter

1.2   c

   5 + 8 + 9 = 22

1.3   d

   4 + 3.2 + 3.2 + 2 = 12.4

1.4   b

   3 + 5 + 4 + 6 = 18

1.5   b

   4 + 4.5 + 4.5 = 13

1.6   a

   2 + 4 + 3 + 5 = 14

1.7   c

   60 + 40 + 60 + 40 = 200

1.8   b

   10 + 4 + 7 + 2 + 5 = 28

1.9   d

   3.5 + 3.5 + 3.5 + 3.5 = 14

1.10   a. 1
   b. 3
   c. 5
   d. 2
   e. 4

1.11   b

1.12   c

   3 × 9 cm = 27 cm

1.13   d

   8 × 7 in = 56 in

1.14   b

   6 sides × 3 m = 18 m

1.15   c

   5 × 8 in = 40 in

1.16   a

   The common perimeter is 24 cm
   (6 × 4 cm = 24 cm).
   24 cm ÷ 8 sides = 3 cm

1.17   c

   2(8) + 2(6) = 16 + 12 = 28

1.18   d

   2(8) + 2(1) = 16 + 2 = 18

1.19   b

   2(8) + 2(9) = 16 + 18 = 34

1.20   a. 1
   b. 3
   c. 4
   d. 5
   e. 2

1.21   a. 1
   b. 4
   c. 2
   d. 3
   e. 5

1.22   b

1.23   b

   3.14 × 4 = 12.56

1.24   b

   $\frac{22}{7} \times 7 = 22$

1.25   a

3 × 9 = 27 (An estimate is *not* rounding the answer.)

1.26   d

d = 2 × 50 mm
d = 100 mm
3.14 × 100 = 314

1.27   b

3 × 15 = 45, but π > 3, so the actual result should be > 45 (more than 15 tenths).

1.28   c

The pizza's diameter is 16 inches;
3.14 × 16 = 50.24

1.29   c

The circumference is 3.14 × 4 = 12.56;
12.56 – 12 = 0.56

1.30   c

$\frac{22}{7} \times 21 = \frac{462}{7} = 66$, or $\frac{22}{7} \times 21 = \frac{21}{7} \times 22 = 3 \times 22 = 66$

1.31   a. 3
      b. 2
      c. 1
      d. 4
      e. 5

SELF TEST 1

1.01   d

8 + 8 + 3 = 19

1.02   b

2.2 + 4.1 + 3 + 3 = 12.3

1.03   d

8 + 5 + 6 + 6 = 25

1.04   c

6 + 6 + 2 = 14

1.05   b

3 + 4 + 2 = 9; 12 – 9 = 3

1.06   d

4 × 8.5 cm = 34 cm

1.07   c

2(6) + 2(2) = 12 + 4 = 16

1.08   b

7 sides × 3 m = 21 m

1.09   c

6 × 7 in = 42 in

1.010   c

2(4) + 2(5) = 8 + 10 = 18

1.011   c

3.14 × 12 = 37.68

1.012   c

$\frac{22}{7} \times 9 = \frac{198}{7} = 28\frac{2}{7}$

1.013 b

> 3 × 18 = 54 (an estimate is *not* rounding the answer)

1.014 c

> d = 2 × 19 m, d = 38 m.
> 3.14 × 38 = 119.32

1.015 b

> 3 × 24 = 72, but π > 3, so the actual result should be > 72 (more than 24 tenths, or 2.4).

SECTION 2

2.1   a. 2
         b. 1

2.2   b

> There are 12 squares inside the figure.

2.3   c

> There are 16 squares inside the figure.

2.4   c

> There are six squares and six half squares inside the figure.

2.5   c

> There are seven squares and two half squares inside the figure.

2.6   c

> The figure has eleven squares and two half squares.

2.7   b, c

> Area is measured in square units, which can include fractional parts.

2.8   c

> Area is measured in square units.

2.9   d

> Area is a two-dimensional measurement.

2.10   a

2.11   c

> There are 30 squares inside the rectangle (10 × 3 = 30).

2.12   d

> 5 × 8 = 40

2.13   b

> 7 × 4 = 28

2.14 d

12.5 × 6 = 75

2.15 a

6 × 7 = 42, 4 × 10 = 40, 6 × 5 = 30,
9 × 4 = 36

2.16 d

12 × 12 = 144

2.17 c

32 ÷ 4 = 8, 8 × 8 = 64

2.18 c

9 × 9 = 81

2.19 a. 6
       b. 4
       c. 2
       d. 8
       e. 7
       f. 1
       g. 3
       h. 5
2.20 a. 2
       b. 1
2.21 c

The parallelogram is 10 units long and
3 units high (10 × 3 = 30).

2.22 d

8 × 12.5 = 100

2.23 b

8 × 10 = 80, 9 × 8 = 72, 10 × 7 = 70,
12 × 6 = 72

2.24 d

7 × 6 = 42

2.25 b

4 × 3 = 12

2.26 b

We don't know how far over the top base
is shifted from the bottom base. Given the
base and height, the figure could even be
a rectangle.

2.27 b

6 × 9 = 54

2.28 b

3 × 12 = 36

2.29 a, b, d

base × height must be 48: 12 × 4 = 48,
6 × 8 = 48, 16 × 3 = 48; 7 × 7 = 49

2.30 a. 5
       b. 7
       c. 3
       d. 4
       e. 8
       f. 6
       g. 1
       h. 2
2.31 a. 2
       b. 1
2.32 c
2.33 a

The base of the triangle is 5 units and the
height is 3 units: (5 × 3) ÷ 2 = 7.5

2.34 b

(6 × 8) ÷ 2 = 24

2.35 b

(5 × 7) ÷ 2 = 17.5, (7 × 4) ÷ 2 = 14,
(3 × 10) ÷ 2 = 15, (6 × 5) ÷ 2 = 15

2.36 c

(10 × 8) ÷ 2 = 40

2.37 a, d

base × height ÷ 2 must be 36:
(12 × 6) ÷ 2 = 36, (8 × 9) ÷ 2 = 36

2.38 b

> The figure divides into a rectangle
> (4 × 3 = 12) and a triangle ((4 × 3) ÷ 2 = 6);
> 12 + 6 = 18.

2.39 b

> 5 × 3 + (5 × 2) ÷ 2 = 15 + 5 = 20

2.40 a

> The triangle base is 4 (7 – 3 = 4);
> (4 × 2) ÷ 2 = 4
> The parallelogram is 3 × 2 = 6;
> 4 + 6 = 10

2.41 b

> We don't know where the top vertex
> is in relation to the base.

2.42 a. 2
   b. 6
   c. 4
   d. 3
   e. 1
   f. 8
   g. 7
   h. 5

SELF TEST 2

2.01 c

> There are 10 squares and 2 half-squares
> inside the figure.

2.02 c

> There are 14 squares inside the figure.

2.03 c

> Area is measured in square units.

2.04 b

> 2 × 9 = 18

2.05 d

> 8 × 10 = 80

2.06 d

> 7.5 × 8 = 60

2.07 c

> 4 × 7 = 28, 5 × 4 = 20, 4 × 6 = 24, 5 × 5 = 25

2.08 d

> 7 × 12 = 84

2.09 a

> 8 × 8 = 64

2.010 c

> 5 × 2 = 10

2.011 b

> 7 × 5 = 35, 6 × 7 = 42, 10 × 4 = 40,
> 4 × 9 = 36

2.012 b

> (7 × 3) ÷ 2 = 10.5

2.013 b

$(6 \times 9) \div 2 = 27$

2.014 c

$(5 \times 3) + (5 \times 2) = 15 + 10 = 25$

2.015 d

The triangle base is 3 (6 – 3 = 3);
$(3 \times 3) \div 2 = 4.5$
The parallelogram is $3 \times 3 = 9$;
$4.5 + 9 = 13.5$

SECTION 3

3.1 net

3.2 d

$2(4 \times 2) + 2(4 \times 2) + 2(2 \times 2) =$
$16 + 16 + 8 = 40$

3.3 d

$6(5 \times 5) = 6 \times 25 = 150$

3.4 a

The front and back faces (orange) are the only square faces.

3.5 c

$2(8 \times 4) + 2(8 \times 4) + 2(4 \times 4) =$
$64 + 64 + 32 = 160$

3.6 d

Each of the areas has a congruent partner, so the surface area is the total of the three given areas doubled: $2(12 + 16 + 20) =$
$2(48) = 96$.

3.7 c

$2(4 \times 3) + 2(4 \times 2) + 2(3 \times 2) =$
$24 + 16 + 12 = 52$

3.8 c

$2(14 \times 14) + 2(14 \times 2) + 2(2 \times 14) =$
$392 + 56 + 56 = 504$

3.9 a

There are six congruent faces: $54 \text{ cm}^2 \div 6$
$= 9 \text{ cm}^2$. If each side is 9 cm^2, then each side must be 3 cm: $3 \text{ cm} \times 3 \text{ cm} = 9 \text{ cm}^2$.

3.10
a. 4
b. 5
c. 2
d. 1
e. 3

3.11
a. 2
b. 1

3.12   b

$4 \times 2 \times 3 = 24$

3.13   d

$7 \times 7 \times 7 = 343$

3.14   c

$3 \times 6 \times 5 = 90$

3.15   b

$8 \times 4 \times 4 = 128$

3.16   d

$3 \times 5 \times 5 = 75$, $4 \times 5 \times 3 = 60$, $3 \times 6 \times 3 = 54$, $6 \times 6 \times 2 = 72$

3.17   b

$3 \times 3 \times 3 = 27$, $4 \times 4 \times 1 = 16$, $2 \times 4 \times 2 = 16$, $1 \times 6 \times 2 = 12$

3.18   b

$4 \times 4 \times 4 = 64$

3.19   c

Volume is measured in cubic units.

3.20   a. 8
b. 5
c. 3
d. 1
e. 6
f. 7
g. 4
h. 2

3.21   b
3.22   b

$4 \times 6 \times 3 = 72$

3.23   d

$4 \times 2 \times 4 = 32$

3.24   c

$72 + 32 = 104$

3.25   c

$4 \times 2 \times 4 = 32$

3.26   c

$40 \times 10 \times 8 = 3{,}200$

3.27   d

$120 \times 30 \times 30 = 108{,}000$

3.28   c

$120 \times 30 \times 60 = 216{,}000$

3.29   c

$108{,}000 + 216{,}000 = 324{,}000$

3.30   d
3.31   c
3.32   d

SELF TEST 3

3.01   c

2(4 × 2) + 2(2 × 4) + 2(4 × 4) =
16 + 16 + 32 = 64

3.02   c

4 × 4 × 2 = 32

3.03   d

2(3 × 4) + 2(3 × 3) + 2(4 × 3) =
24 + 18 + 24 = 66

3.04   b

2 × 5 × 7 = 70

3.05   a

Surface area is measured in square units.

3.06   d

Area of 1 face = 4 × 4 = 16,
16 × 6 faces = 96.

3.07   c

4 × 9 × 3 = 108, 6 × 4 × 4 = 96,
7 × 3 × 5 = 105, 5 × 6 × 3= 90

3.08   d

Volume is measured in cubic units.

3.09   d

The area of 1 face is 100: 600 ÷ 6 = 100,
so each side is 10 (10 × 10 = 100);
10 × 10 × 10 = 1,000.

3.010   c

2(4 × 12) + 2(4 × 2) + 2(12 × 2) =
96 + 16 + 48 = 160

3.011   c

5 × 2 × 2 = 20

3.012   d

6 × 4 × 2 = 48

3.013   d

20 + 48 = 68

3.014   c

25 × 10 × 2 = 500

3.015   a

9 × 7 × 4 = 252;
252 × 0.1 = $25.20

SECTION 4

4.1   a. 5
        b. 8
        c. 2
        d. 6
        e. 4
        f. 1
        g. 3
        h. 7

4.2   b

$$2(4) + 2(7) = 8 + 14 = 22$$

4.3   a

Perimeter is measured in linear units.

4.4   b

$$3.14 \times 18 = 56.52$$

4.5   c

$$4 \times 7 = 28$$

4.6   d

$$8 \times 3 = 24$$

4.7   a

$$(4 \times 3) \div 2 = 12 \div 2 = 6$$

4.8   d

There are 20 squares and 3 half-squares:
20 + 1.5 = 21.5

4.9   c

$$2(4 \times 3) + 2(4 \times 3) = 2(4 \times 4) =$$
$$24 + 24 + 32 = 80$$

4.10   b

$$4 \times 4 \times 3 = 48$$

4.11   d

$$(4 \times 4 \times 2) + (6 \times 6 \times 2) = 32 + 72 = 104$$

4.12   c

Area is measured in square units.

4.13   d

Volume is measured in cubic units.

LIFEPAC TEST

1. c

    $3 + 7 + 3 + 7 = 20$

2. b

    $4 + 3.5 + 5 + 2.5 = 15$

3. c

    $8 \times 6 \text{ in} = 48 \text{ in}$

4. c

    $2(7) + 2(2) = 14 + 4 = 18$

5. b

    $6 \text{ sides} \times 4 \text{ m} = 24 \text{ m}$

6. c

    $3.14 \times 12 = 37.68$

7. b

    There are 13 squares and 2 half-squares inside the figure.

8. b

    $2 \times 12 = 24$

9. d

    $9 \times 10 = 90$

10. c

    $6 \times 10.5 = 63$

11. b

    $7 \times 2 = 14$

12. c

    $(9 \times 10) \div 2 = 45$

13. c

    The triangle base is 3 $(6 - 3 = 3)$;
    $(3 \times 4) \div 2 = 6$.
    The parallelogram is $3 \times 4 = 12$;
    $6 + 12 = 18$.

14. c

    $(6 \times 2) + (6 \times 2) = 12 + 12 = 24$

15. d

    $2(3 \times 6) + 2(4 \times 6) + 2(3 \times 4) =$
    $36 + 48 + 24 = 108$

16. c

    $4 \times 6 \times 3 = 72$

17. d

    There are 6 faces, each 2×2:
    $6 \times 2 \times 2 = 24$.

18. c

    $5 \times 5 \times 10 = 250$

19. c

    $(4 \times 6 \times 3) + (2 \times 2 \times 2) =$
    $72 + 8 = 80$

20. a. 2
    b. 1
    c. 3

    Linear units are used for perimeter.
    Square units are used for surface area.
    Cubic units are used for volume.

ALTERNATE LIFEPAC TEST

1. b

   $4 + 6 + 7 + 5 = 22$

2. b

   $3 + 3.5 + 2 + 5.5 = 14$

3. b

   $7 \times 4 \text{ in} = 28 \text{ in}$

4. b

   $2(9) + 2(3) = 18 + 6 = 24$

5. c

   $10 \text{ sides} \times 7 \text{ m} = 70 \text{ m}$

6. c

   $3.14 \times 6 = 18.84$

7. b

   There are 13 squares and 4 half-squares inside the figure.

8. c

   $6 \times 9 = 54$

9. a

   $9 \times 7 = 63$

10. c

    $6.5 \times 8 = 52$

11. a

    $6 \times 2 = 12$

12. b

    $(9 \times 8) \div 2 = 36$

13. b

    The triangle base is 2 (5 – 3 = 2);
    $(2 \times 3) \div 2 = 3$.
    The parallelogram is $3 \times 3 = 9$;
    $3 + 9 = 12$.

14. c

    $(8 \times 2) + ((8 \times 2) \div 2) = 16 + 8 = 24$

15. c

    $2(8 \times 2) + 2(8 \times 3) + 2(2 \times 3) =$
    $32 + 48 + 12 = 92$

16. c

    $2 \times 8 \times 3 = 48$

17. d

    There are 6 faces, each 4×4:
    $6 \times 4 \times 4 = 96$.

18. d

    $5 \times 10 \times 2 = 100$

19. c

    $(4 \times 6 \times 2) + (4 \times 4 \times 2) =$
    $48 + 32 = 80$

20. a. 2
    b. 1
    c. 3

    Linear units are used for perimeter.
    Square units are used for surface area.
    Cubic units are used for volume.

MATH 510
ALTERNATE LIFEPAC TEST

NAME _____

DATE _____

SCORE _____

Each numbered question = 5 points

Circle the correct letter and answer.

1. Which quadrilateral with side lengths shown will have a perimeter of 22 meters?
   a. 4 m, 5 m, 4 m, 5 m
   b. 4 m, 6 m, 7 m, 5 m
   c. 5 m, 3 m, 9 m, 4 m
   d. 5 m, 5 m, 5 m, 5 m

2. The perimeter of this quadrilateral is 14 meters. What is the length of the unlabeled side?
   a. 5 m
   b. 5.5 m
   c. 6 m
   d. 6.5 m

   2 m

   3 m

   3.5 m

3. What is the perimeter of a regular heptagon with side length 4 inches?
   a. 24 inches   b. 28 inches   c. 32 inches   d. 36 inches

4. What is the perimeter of this rectangle?
   a. 12 feet
   b. 24 feet
   c. 27 feet
   d. 36 feet

   9 ft

   3 ft

5. The perimeter of a regular decagon is 70 m. How long is each side?
   a. 5 m   b. 6 m   c. 7 m   d. 10 m

6. What is the circumference of this circle? (use 3.14 for π)
   a. 9.42 cm
   b. 18 cm
   c. 18.84 cm
   d. 37.68 cm

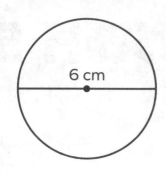

6 cm

7. What is the area of the figure shown here?
   a. 13 square units
   b. 15 square units
   c. 16 square units
   d. 17 square units

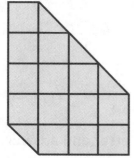

8. What is the area of a rectangle that is 6 meters long and 9 meters wide?
   a. 15 m²   b. 30 m²   c. 54 m²   d. 60 m²

9. The area of a rectangle is 63 ft². If the rectangle is 9 feet long, what is its width?
   a. 7 feet   b. 8 feet   c. 9 feet   d. 10 feet

10. What is the area of a parallelogram with a height of 6.5 feet and a base of 8 feet?
    a. 29 ft²   b. 48 ft²   c. 52 ft²   d. 54 ft²

11. What is the area of the parallelogram shown here?
    a. 12 in²
    b. 16 in²
    c. 20 in²
    d. 24 in²

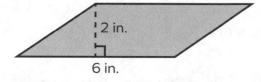

2 in.

6 in.

12. What is the area of a triangle with a base of 9 feet and a height of 8 feet?
    a. 17 ft²   b. 36 ft²   c. 72 ft²   d. 144 ft²

13. What is the area of this trapezoid?
    a. 8 cm²
    b. 12 cm²
    c. 15 cm²
    d. 16 cm²

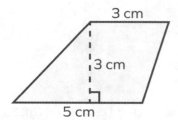

3 cm

3 cm

5 cm

14. What is the area of the pentagon shown here?
    a. 16 m²
    b. 20 m²
    c. 24 m²
    d. 32 m²

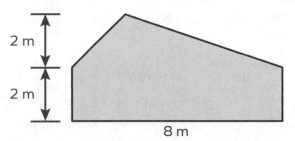

15. What is the surface area of the rectangular prism shown here?
    a. 24 in²
    b. 48 in²
    c. 92 in²
    d. 96 in²

16. What is the volume of the rectangular prism from Question 15?
    a. 16 in³
    b. 24 in³
    c. 48 in³
    d. 92 in³

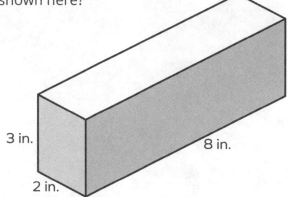

17. What is the surface area of a cube that has sides 4 cm long?
    a. 16 cm²   b. 24 cm²   c. 64 cm²   d. 96 cm²

18. What is the volume of a rectangular prism with the following dimensions?
    h = 5 ft, w = 10 ft, l = 2 ft
    a. 25 ft³   b. 50 ft³   c. 70 ft³   d. 100 ft³

19. What is the volume of the solid figure shown here?
    a. 48 cm³
    b. 72 cm³
    c. 80 cm³
    d. 96 cm³

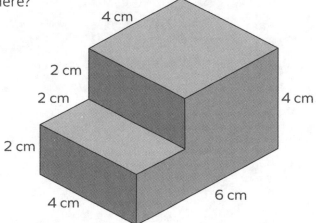

20. Match the measures with the correct type of measurement.

a. _____ 72 m   1. volume

b. _____ 125 mm^3 2. perimeter

c. _____ 50 cm^2 3. surface area

MATH TERMS GLOSSARY

a.m. .... Before midday.

acute angle .... An angle measuring less than 90 degrees.

acute triangle .... A triangle with no angle measuring 90 degrees or more.

addend .... A number to be added.

algebra .... A branch of mathematics that uses variables.

analog clock .... A clock that uses hands to display the time.

angle .... Two rays with a common endpoint.

area .... The measurement of the space inside a plane figure.

arithmetic sequence .... A set of numbers where the difference is the same between any two consecutive terms.

Associative Property of Addition ..... A property of the whole numbers that states that how numbers are grouped in a sum does not change the value.

Associative Property of Multiplication .... A property of numbers that states that how numbers are grouped in a product does not change the value of the product.

bar graph .... A graph used to compare quantities that are represented by bars.

base .... The number that is repeated as a factor in an exponential expression.

base .... The length of a plane figure.

base .... A special face of a solid figure.

biased question .... A question that leads individuals toward a certain answer.

biased sample .... A sample not representative of the entire population.

capacity .... The amount a container can hold.

categorical data .... Data grouped using non-numerical criteria.

Celsius .... The international temperature scale; water freezes at 0 degrees C and boils at 100 degrees C.

centi- .... Prefix meaning one-hundredth.

centimeter .... One-hundredth of a meter.

chord .... A line segment that connects two points on a circle.

circle .... A figure with all of its points the same distance from the center.

circumference .... The distance around the outside of a circle.

Commutative Property of Addition .... A property of the whole numbers that states that the order in which numbers are added does not change the value.

Commutative Property of Multiplication ... A property of numbers that states that the order in which numbers are multiplied does not change the value of the product.

compatible numbers .... Numbers that are easy to compute with.

composite number .... A number that has more factors than just 1 and itself.

cone .... A three-dimensional figure with a circular base.

congruent .... Having the same exact size and shape.

congruent figures .... Polygons that have the same size and shape.

coordinate plane .... A two-dimensional system in which a location is described by its distance from two intersecting, perpendicular axes.

corresponding angles .... Angles in the same position on similar figures.

corresponding parts .... Angles or sides in the same position on similar figures.

corresponding sides .... Sides in the same position on similar figures.

cube .... A three-dimensional figure made of six congruent squares.

cubic units .... Units used to measure the volume of a three-dimensional figure.

cylinder .... A three-dimensional figure with two parallel, congruent, circular bases and a curved surface.

data pair .... Two values in a data set that are dependent on each other.

deca- .... Prefix meaning ten.

decagon .... A polygon with ten sides.

deci- .... Prefix meaning one-tenth.

decimal number .... A special fraction based on the number ten.

decimal point .... The period in a decimal number that separates the whole from the part of a whole.

degrees .... The unit of angle measure.

denominator .... The number under the fraction bar; tells how many equal parts the whole was broken into.

density .... The amount of mass an object has, compared to its volume.

diameter .... A line segment that goes through the center of a circle to connect two points on the circle.

difference .... The result of subtracting two numbers.

digit .... One of the numerals from 0 to 9.

digital clock .... A clock that shows the time using digits.

Distributive Property .... A number multiplied by a sum is the same as the sum of the number multiplied by each addend; $a(b + c) = ab + ac$.

dividend .... The number being divided.

divisible .... Able to be divided evenly, without a remainder.

divisor .... The number of parts that the dividend is being divided into.

dodecagon .... A polygon with twelve sides.

edge .... A line segment where two faces meet.

elapsed time .... The amount of time between two events.

endpoint .... A point that marks the end of a line segment or ray.

equation .... A mathematical statement that shows two expressions are equal using an equal sign.

equilateral .... Having sides of equal length.

equilateral triangle .... A triangle whose three sides all are the same length.

equivalent fractions .... Fractions with the same numerical value; fractions that are equal to each other.

estimate .... An approximate value that is close to the actual value.

event .... A specific outcome or group of outcomes.

expanded form .... Shows a number written as an addition statement.

experimental probability .... A ratio representing the actual results of an experiment.

exponent .... The smaller number in an exponential expression; tells how many times a factor is repeated.

expression	A single term; multiple terms connected by an addition or subtraction sign.
face	A plane figure that is one side of a solid figure.
factor	A number to be multiplied.
factor	A number that divides evenly into another number.
factor tree	An organized way of finding the prime factorization of a number.
Fahrenheit	The temperature scale used in the United States; water freezes at 32 degrees F and boils at 212 degrees F.
family of facts	All possible combinations for a set of numbers (2 + 3 = 5, 3 + 2 = 5, 5 − 3 = 2, 5 − 2 = 3).
fraction	A number that shows part of a whole.
fraction bar	The line between the numerator and denominator of a fraction.
function	A relation in which for any given input value, there is only one output value.
gram	The basic metric unit for mass.
greater than	When one number is larger in value than another.
greatest common factor	The largest factor that any given numbers have in common.
hecto-	Prefix meaning one hundred.
height	The perpendicular width of a plane figure.
heptagon	A polygon with seven sides.
hexagon	A polygon with six sides.
Identity Property of Addition	A property of the whole numbers that states that adding zero to a number does not change the value of the number.
Identity Property of Multiplication	A property of numbers that states that multiplying a number by 1 does not change the value of the number.
image	A shape or object that has been transformed.
improper fraction	A fraction in which the numerator is larger than or equal to the denominator.
independent events	Compound events in which one event does not affect the likelihood of the other event.

input	A value that is substituted in for the variable in a function in order to generate an output value.
integer	A number belonging to the set made up of the whole numbers and their opposites.
International System of Units	The primary system of measurement used by most countries in the world; the modern metric system of measurement; abbreviated SI.
intersecting lines	Lines in the same plane that are not parallel.
inverse operations	Opposite operations that undo one another.
irregular polygon	Any polygon that is not regular.
isosceles trapezoid	A trapezoid with non-parallel sides congruent.
isosceles triangle	A triangle with at least two equal sides.
kilo-	Prefix meaning one thousand.
kilogram	One thousand grams.
kilometer	One thousand meters.
lateral face	Any face that is not a base.
lateral surface	Any surface that is not a base.
least common denominator	The smallest number that all the given denominators divide into evenly.
least common multiple	The smallest multiple that any given numbers have in common.
less than	When one number is smaller in value than another.
like denominators	Denominators that are the same number.
line	An infinite set of points forming a straight path that continues in both directions.
line graph	Graph comparing two variables; often shows change in a quantity over time.
line of reflection	The mirror line; the line across which a figure is flipped.
line of symmetry	The line which divides a figure into two congruent mirror images.
line plot	A graph showing frequency of data on a number line.
line segment	A part of a line bounded by two endpoints.
line symmetry	Property where a figure can be folded along a line to create two congruent mirror images.

liter	The basic metric unit for capacity.
long division	A method for dividing with larger numbers that breaks the process into smaller steps.
mass	The amount of matter in an object.
mean	The sum of a set of data divided by the number of items in the set.
median	The middle value of a set of data arranged in numerical order.
meter	The basic metric unit for length.
milli-	Prefix meaning one-thousandth.
milligram	One-thousandth of a gram.
milliliter	One-thousandth of a liter.
millimeter	One-thousandth of a meter.
mixed number	A number with a whole number part and a fraction part.
mode	The most frequently occurring number(s) in a data set.
multiple	The product of a number and another nonzero whole number.
multiple of ten	A number formed by multiplying ten by a number.
natural number	A number belonging to the set made up of the counting numbers: 1, 2, 3, and so on.
negative number	A number that is less than zero.
net	A two-dimensional representation of a three-dimensional shape when unfolded.
number line	A line that graphically represents all numbers.
numerator	The number above the fraction bar; tells how many parts of the whole exist.
numerical data	Data represented by quantities.
obtuse angle	An angle measuring greater than 90 degrees.
obtuse triangle	A triangle with one angle that measures more than 90 degrees.
octagon	A polygon with eight sides.
opposite numbers	Two numbers that are the same distance from zero on the number line but in opposite directions.

ordered pair .... A group of two numbers written in the order (x, y), where the first value represents the input for a function and the second value represents the corresponding output.

order of operations .... A system for simplifying expressions that ensures that there is only one right answer.

origin .... The intersection of the x-axis and y-axis.

outcome .... Any possible results of an experiment.

output .... A value generated by a function when an input value is substituted into the function and evaluated.

overestimate .... An estimate that is higher than the actual value.

p.m. .... After midday.

parallel lines .... Lines in the same plane that do not intersect.

parallelogram .... A quadrilateral with two sets of parallel, congruent sides.

partial product .... The product of one digit of a factor and one digit of the other factor.

pentagon .... A polygon with five sides.

perimeter .... The distance around the outside of a plane figure.

period .... Each three-digit part of a whole number, separated by commas.

perpendicular lines .... Lines that intersect and create right angles.

place value .... The position of a digit in a number, which determines its value.

plane .... A flat surface that continues in all directions.

point .... A position in space.

polygon .... A closed figure made up of line segments.

positive number .... A number that is greater than zero.

power of ten .... Number formed by raising 10 to an exponent.

pre-image .... The original shape or object that is being transformed.

prime factorization .... The product of prime factors of a number.

prime number .... A number that has only two factors: 1 and itself.

prism .... A three-dimensional figure with two parallel, congruent, polygonal faces and parallelograms for all other faces.

probability .... A measure of the likelihood of an event.

product .... The result of multiplying two or more numbers.

proper fraction .... A fraction in which the numerator is smaller than the denominator.

protractor .... A tool used to measure angles.

pyramid .... A three-dimensional figure with one polygon base, and triangular faces meeting at a common vertex.

quadrilateral .... A polygon with four sides.

quotient .... The result of dividing two numbers.

radius .... A line segment from the center of a circle to any point on the circle.

range .... The difference between the largest and smallest data points.

ray .... A part of a line that has one endpoint and continues in one direction.

rectangle .... A parallelogram with four right angles.

reflection .... A transformation in which a figure is flipped across a line to give a mirror image of the original figure.

regular polygon .... A polygon whose sides are all congruent.

remainder .... The amount left over after dividing two numbers.

rhombus .... A parallelogram with four congruent sides.

right angle .... An angle measuring 90 degrees.

right triangle .... A triangle with one angle that measures 90 degrees.

rotation .... A transformation in which a figure turns around a fixed center point.

rotational symmetry .... The property that allows a figure to be rotated less than 360 degrees and still look the same; also referred to as *point symmetry*.

rounding .... Changing a number to one that is less exact, so it is easier to work with.

sample space .... An organized listing of all possible outcomes for an experiment.

scalene triangle .... A triangle with no sides equal.

sequence .... A list of numbers.

similar figures .... Polygons that have the same shape but not necessarily the same size.

simplest form	A fraction in lowest terms.
solid figure	A geometric figure with three dimensions.
sphere	The set of all points that are a given distance from a center point in any direction.
square	A parallelogram with 4 right angles and 4 congruent sides.
square units	The unit of measure for area.
standard form	Shows a number written using digits.
straight angle	An angle measuring 180 degrees.
substitute	To replace a variable in a mathematical expression with an actual value.
sum	The result of adding two or more numbers.
surface area	The total area of all the faces or surfaces of a three-dimensional figure.
term	A member (or number) in a sequence.
thermometer	An instrument used to measure temperature.
transformation	A change made to a shape or object.
translation	A transformation in which a figure is slid to a new location.
trapezoid	A quadrilateral with one pair of parallel sides.
U.S. Customary System of Units	The primary system of measurement used in the United States.
underestimate	An estimate that is lower than the actual value.
unit fraction	A fraction that has a 1 in the numerator.
unlike denominators	Denominators that are different numbers.
variable	A letter used to represent an unknown number or quantity.
vertex	A point where three or more edges meet.
volume	The amount of space inside a three-dimensional figure.
weight	The force on an object from gravity.
whole number	A number belonging to the set of numbers made up of zero and the counting numbers: 1, 2, 3, and so on.
whole number property	A characteristic of the whole numbers.
word form	Shows a number written in words.

x-axis .... The horizontal axis on the coordinate plane.

x-coordinate .... The horizontal distance from the *y*-axis; written first in an ordered pair.

y-axis .... The vertical axis on the coordinate plane.

y-coordinate .... The vertical distance from the *x*-axis; written second in an ordered pair.

Zero Property of Multiplication .... A property of numbers that states that the product of any number and zero is zero.

METRIC CHART OF PREFIXES

(smallest)	milli-	a unit contains 1,000
	centi-	a unit contains 100
	deci-	a unit contains 10
	unit	unit (meter, liter, gram)
	deca-	contains 10 units
	hecto-	contains 100 units
(largest)	kilo-	contains 1,000 units

ENGLISH SYSTEM OF WEIGHTS AND MEASURES

Length	Weight	Dry Measure	Liquid Measure
12 inches = 1 foot	16 ounces = 1 pound	2 cups = 1 pint	16 fl. ounces = 1 pint
3 feet = 1 yard	2,000 lbs. = 1 ton	2 pints = 1 quart	2 cups = 1 pint
36 inches = 1 yard		8 quarts = 1 peck	2 pints = 1 quart
5,280 feet = 1 mile		4 pecks = 1 bushel	4 quarts = 1 gallon
320 rods = 1 mile			

CONVERSION CHART

To convert	To	Multiply by	To convert	To	Multiply by
Linear Measure					
centimeters	inches	.394	inches	centimeters	2.54
meters	yards	1.0936	yards	meters	.914
kilometers	miles	.62	miles	kilometers	1.609
Liquid Measure					
liters	quarts	1.057	quarts	liters	.946
Dry Measure					
liters	quarts	.908	quarts	liters	1.101
Weight					
grams	ounces	.0353	ounces	grams	28.35
kilograms	pounds	2.2046	pounds	kilograms	.4536